POTATO PRODUCTION

POTATO
PRODUCTION

E. V. Hardenburg, PH.D.

PROFESSOR OF VEGETABLE CROPS, NEW YORK STATE
COLLEGE OF AGRICULTURE AT CORNELL UNIVERSITY

Comstock Publishing Company, INC.

ITHACA, NEW YORK, 1949

Copyright 1949 by Comstock Publishing Company, Inc.

PRINTED IN THE UNITED STATES OF AMERICA BY THE
VAIL-BALLOU PRESS, INC., BINGHAMTON, NEW YORK

To my wife, L. Aline Crandall,
for help and encouragement

Preface

THE commercial importance of potato production and interest in it are presupposed in the preparation of a text on this subject. The potato is the most widely grown and consumed of a long list of vegetables. It is the only one so universally eaten as to be considered a staple food. Of the total annual per-capita consumption, in the United States, of 368 pounds of vegetables, potatoes represent a little over one-third. The crop is grown commercially in every one of the forty-eight states, and its total farm value in the United States during the years 1945–1947 inclusive averaged about six hundred million dollars.

The author's primary purpose in attempting a work of this kind is to prepare a text for college students. He hopes that it will also be of interest and use to students and teachers of secondary-school agriculture, to extension agents, to commercial interests who serve the potato industry, and to growers and handlers of potatoes.

Although technical publications concerning the potato are numerous and generally useful, many of them are not up-to-date in their consideration of the relation of environment and cultural treatment to the practices and situations of the present day. The fact of change itself creates a continuing problem for the investigator, the student, and the grower. The author fully realizes that the facts of today will in part be superseded by other facts tomorrow. His task has been largely one of selecting, sorting, and analyzing the mass of material available. However, the author has had the encouragement which comes from working with hundreds of successful growers, with several generations of college students, and with co-workers in many states. A usable text covering all phases of potato production and marketing must present in concise, organized, and understandable form not only the conditions common to the various regions of the United States but also the recurring problems, the methods by which they have been investigated, and the results and practices that seem worthy of adoption in a rapidly changing agriculture. Whatever satisfaction may result from the effort will be measured in terms of the increased ease and profit with which the reader and particularly the student can acquaint himself with the subject.

Free use has been made of bulletins published by state experiment stations and the United States Department of Agriculture and of numerous articles by scientific societies. The author appreciates the generous facilities of the Department of Vegetable Crops of the New York State College of Agriculture and the help and encouragement of his colleagues, especially Professors H. C. Thompson, Paul Work, Ora Smith, and A. J. Pratt of that department, and of Professors M. C. Bond of the Department of Agricultural Economics and H. H. Schwardt of the Department of Entomology. He is grateful to Professor A. M. Goodman for advice with the chapter on storage, to Professor W. A. Rawlins for advice and help with the chapter on insects and other pests, to Professor E. S. Phillips and Mrs. Audrey H. O'Connor of the Department of Extension Teaching for many of the illustrations, and to Mrs. Olladene Wortman for typing most of the manuscript. Interpretations of many of the experiments cited are the author's, and he accepts full responsibility for them.

Ithaca, New York   E. V. HARDENBURG
October, 1948

Contents

POTATO PRODUCTION

CHAPTER 1

Economic Importance

FOOD PRODUCTION in any region is necessarily limited by such factors as climate, soil, and the economic status of the inhabitants. Potato production is largely limited to the north temperate zone where the climate is fairly cool and moist. The potato is grown for its edible underground tuber which supplies a cheap, bulky, nutritious, healthful, carbohydrate food to at least one-third of the world's total population.

Rank as a Food Crop

Among the world's most important food crops, the potato ranks first in terms of volume of the fresh product. Because in China, Japan, and other Asiatic countries more people depend on rice as a staple than depend on potatoes, rice outranks potatoes in terms of population fed. In recent years, in northern China, emphasis on the production and consumption of potatoes has been increasing to give greater efficiency in food production and greater diversity in the diet. Next to potatoes and rice, the cereal grains, wheat, corn, and oats, are of major importance as world food crops. The rank of potatoes in bushels produced annually, both in the world and in the United States for the 5-year period 1935–1939, in comparison with that of other important food crops, is shown in table 1.

Origin and History

Records of the region or country in which the potato was first found and used as food are not clear. This is because either the sources of information were confused as to the species of plant being described, or they depended on the memory of some traveler who shipped with such explorers and colonizers as Sir Francis Drake and Sir Walter Raleigh. Some authors state that the potato was first found either on the high plateaus of Bolivia and Peru or on

the island of Chiloe and the adjacent mainland of Chile. It was first
recorded in literature by a Spaniard named Pedro de Cieze de Leon,
in *Chronicles of Peru* in 1553. He claimed to have found the potato
in 1538 in Colombia and later Ecuador, where it was being grown
by South American Indians under the name "papas."

TABLE 1. WORLD AND UNITED STATES PRODUCTION OF
IMPORTANT FOOD CROPS * (AVERAGE 1935–1939 †).

Crop	World		United States	
	Thousand Bushels	Per cent of World Total	Thousand Bushels	Per cent of U.S. Total
Potatoes	8,126,500	23.4	355,513	7.4
Rice	7,447,000	21.4	49,852	1.0
Wheat	5,914,000	17.2	758,623	15.8
Corn	4,721,000	13.6	2,315,539	48.2
Oats	4,362,000	12.6	1,045,329	21.7
Barley	2,338,000	6.8	238,616	5.0
Rye	1,728,000	5.0	44,917	0.9
Total	34,636,500	100.0	4,808,389	100.0

* Compiled from data in *Agricultural Statistics,* U.S. Dept. of Agriculture, 1946.
† Figures for later years are incomplete for several important producing countries.

The wild, bitter-tubered species found in Chile is presumably
Solanum maglia, but the species cultivated there, like that now
grown in the United States, is *S. tuberosum.* The species native to
the Bolivia-Peruvian plateau is recorded as *S. andigenum.* According to Balls (1942), the most widely cultivated species of Solanum
found in Central and South America are *S. demissum* in Mexico,
S. acaule in Argentina, and *S. andigenum* in Bolivia and Peru. Although the species mentioned above have been used to improve
S. tuberosum in both Europe and North America, the species
tuberosum is the one most widely cultivated in the world today. In
the temperate zones *S. tuberosum* develops large tubers.

Techniques now used in the United States for dehydration and
the manufacture of potato starch and flour are really not new. The
Indians of the high plateaus of South America have for centuries
preserved the potato as a product called *chunu* or *chunyo,* from

which they make bread. A Jesuit missionary, Bernabe Cobo, wrote (1571–1576):

The tubers are gathered at the beginning of the cold season, in May or June, spread out on the ground and exposed for a period of twelve or fifteen days, to the sun during the day and the frost at night. At the end of this time they are somewhat shriveled, but still watery. In order to get rid of the water they are then trampled upon and then left for fifteen or twenty days longer to the action of the sun and frost, at length becoming dry and light as cork.

The potato has an interesting history as a world traveler, for although native to the Americas it was first introduced to North America from Europe. It came into Europe by way of Spain, Italy, and Germany soon after the Spanish conquest of Peru about the middle

Fig. 1. A large level field of Katahdin potatoes in bloom in Steuben County, New York.

of the sixteenth century. It did not reach commercial importance in Europe until the latter part of the seventeenth century; it was first grown in Great Britain in 1662 but was found mostly in home gardens until about 1740. Doubt as to whether it was safe to eat greatly delayed its acceptance as a human food. It was extensively used by the peasant class in Ireland before being used by the more aristocratic people of England. This is evidenced by the occurrence of the Irish famine of 1845, when an epiphytotic of the late blight disease destroyed the chief source of food of the Irish people and caused many of them to emigrate to America.

The potato was first grown in North America in 1719 by a group of Irish Presbyterians at the time they founded the town of Londonderry, New Hampshire. Records indicate that, somewhat later, the colonists who founded the Jamestown colony introduced the potato into Virginia. From these points potato culture has spread, and the potato has become an important food staple throughout North America from southern Florida and south Texas to places within the Arctic Circle in Alaska and Canada.

Consumption in Relation to Other Vegetables

When the United States was a new country, its population had much less choice of food and therefore depended more on such staples as potatoes, beans, cereals, meat, and poultry products. According to *Agricultural Statistics* (1946), the consumption of energy foods like the potato has been steadily decreasing in the United States, while the consumption of fresh vegetables, foods containing essential minerals and vitamins, and fat has been increasing during the 36-year period 1909–1945. While this trend may be justified, it is not conducive to an increased consumption of potatoes. The increased consumption of fresh, canned, and frozen vegetables and citrus fruit has very probably been responsible for a corresponding decrease in potato consumption. The trend of per-capita consumption of these two major classes of vegetables during the period 1929–1945 is shown in table 2.

Consumption of potatoes is very much greater in Germany, Poland, France, Belgium, Holland, and the Scandinavian countries of Europe than it is in the United States. Because potatoes are a staple rather than a luxury food in this country, fluctuation in farm prices, general price level, or purchasing power of our people seem to bear very little relation to per-capita consumption.

Production by World Countries

The potato is well adapted to the cool, humid climate of northern Europe, and total production and average yields are much higher there than in America. Even though production involves a comparatively high labor cost, cheap labor in these Old World countries makes it feasible to grow potatoes mostly with hand labor. Largely because of the cool growing-season temperatures available in Germany, Czechoslovakia, Belgium, Netherlands, Austria, and the United Kingdom, yields average higher than in Italy, Spain, the Soviet Union, France, and the United States. Of a total of more than 8 billion bushels produced annually in the world, more than 80 per cent are grown in Europe alone. Even though the potato is the most

TABLE 2. ANNUAL AVERAGE PER-CAPITA CONSUMPTION OF POTATOES AND OTHER VEGETABLES IN THE UNITED STATES, 1929–1945.*

Year	Pounds per Capita		Year	Pounds per Capita	
	Potatoes	Other Vegetables †		Potatoes	Other Vegetables †
1929	155	223	1938	132	247
1930	136	213	1939	121	242
1931	140	222	1940	130	239
1932	139	227	1941	128	241
1933	137	213	1942	125	251
1934	138	218	1943	133	236
1935	144	230	1944	128	255
1936	132	219	1945	129	268
1937	126	235	Unweighted Average	134	234

* Adapted from table 337, *Agricultural Statistics*, U.S. Dept. of Agriculture, 1946.
† All fresh vegetables, including melons, but excluding potatoes, sweet potatoes, and dry beans.

important vegetable in the United States, this country produces annually only about 4.4 per cent of the world total. The average annual acreage, production, and yield of potatoes for those countries producing more than 100 million bushels annually during the 5-year period 1935–1939 are shown in table 3.

Production in the United States

During the early history of the United States, commercial potato production was centered in the New England and Middle Atlantic States. New York, Pennsylvania, Maine, Vermont, and New Jersey furnished most of the surplus crop for the larger city markets. Vermont, New York, Massachusetts, New Jersey, and Pennsylvania

TABLE 3. POTATO PRODUCTION IN WORLD COUNTRIES (FIVE-YEAR AVERAGE, 1935–1939 *).

Country	Acreage (in Thousands)	Production (Thousand Bushels)	Yield per Acre (Bushels)
Soviet Union	17,569	2,134,300	121.5
Germany	7,160	1,835,875	256.4
Poland	7,312	1,040,294	142.3
France	3,489	573,225	164.9
Czechoslovakia	1,879	372,677	198.3
United States	3,033	355,513	117.2
United Kingdom	719	182,666	254.1
Spain	1,126	170,977	151.8
Belgium	383	116,872	305.1
Austria	520	106,037	203.9
Italy	1,041	100,917	96.9
Netherlands	323	100,747	311.9
World	52,280	8,126,500	155.4

* From *Agricultural Statistics,* U.S. Dept. of Agriculture, 1946.

were the birthplaces of nearly all of our varieties of first importance. Varieties imported from Europe and from the South and Central American countries proved to be of little or no value for our climatic and seasonal conditions. Areas of commercial importance developed westward with the opening of new land and in those localities where cool, humid conditions prevailed. In some areas where favorable soil and temperature were available but rainfall was deficient, as in Colorado, Idaho, and Southern California, irrigation water supplied the deficiency and made these states important producers of potatoes. Prior to 1870, little was known about the control of the late blight disease, *Phytophthora infestans,* and this disease proved a serious handicap to expansion of the industry. Popular literature dealt at length with many and various theories concerning the nature and control of the so-called potato plague.

Production in the United States showed a steady growth from about 66 million bushels in 1849 to 395 million bushels in 1909. During this period, many new and better varieties, a control for the late blight disease, and numerous labor saving devices were

Fig. 2. Warba, an early variety, does well on muck soil in Genesee County, New York.

developed. Potato acreage, production, and yields by 5-year periods for the 55 years from 1890 to 1944 inclusive are shown in table 4 and graphs I and II.

It is obvious that potato acreage in the United States reached a peak about 1915–1919. The increased demands for food during World War I may have been partly responsible for this increase in

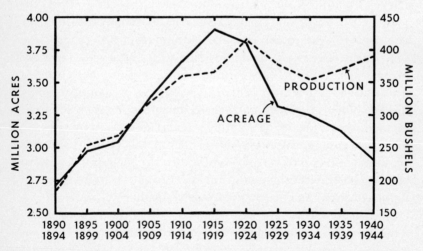

Graph I. Potato acreage and production in the United States by 5-year periods, 1890–1944.

acreage. Actually the largest acreage ever planted up to date was 4,384,000 in 1917, and this may be compared with 2,578,000 in 1946, the smallest acreage since before 1890. In spite of this decrease in acreage in recent years, total production has been maintained at

TABLE 4. POTATO ACREAGE, PRODUCTION, AND YIELD IN THE UNITED STATES, 1890–1944, BY 5-YEAR PERIODS.

5-Year Period	Acreage (Thousands)	Production (Million Bushels)	Yield per Acre (Bushels)
1890–1894	2729.6	190.0	69.6
1895–1899	2933.8	251.8	85.4
1900–1904	3062.6	270.9	88.2
1905–1909	3397.2	326.0	95.8
1910–1914	3685.8	360.7	97.8
1915–1919	3904.0	364.7	92.9
1920–1924	3806.2	410.8	108.6
1925–1929	3369.0	380.5	112.6
1930–1934	3254.4	353.8	108.7
1935–1939	3167.2	368.9	116.5
1940–1944	2903.0	390.0	134.3
55-Year Average	3292.1	333.5	101.3

a level usually above 350 million bushels, reaching a record of 474,609,000 bushels in 1946. This reflects the steadily increasing average acre yield shown in graph II. The record average yield was 184.1 bushels in 1946, made possible by an abnormally long growing season, exceptionally favorable weather in most areas, and widespread use of a new insecticide called DDT.

The comparative rank of the fifteen leading states on the basis of average annual production for the 5-year period 1941–1945 is shown in table 5. In recent years California, Idaho, New Jersey, North Carolina, and North Dakota have shown the most rapid expansion of acreage. The leading potato counties, based on acreage according to the census of 1945, are Aroostook in Maine, Kern in California, Suffolk in New York, and Walsh and Grand Forks in North Dakota. This indicates how widely scattered are the most intensive production areas. Five-year average yields for the fifteen leading states during 1941–1945 vary from 85 bushels in Wisconsin to 312 bushels in

California. Whereas the high average yield in Maine is largely due to an ideal climate and soil, the yields recorded for Colorado, California, and Idaho are made possible by irrigation.

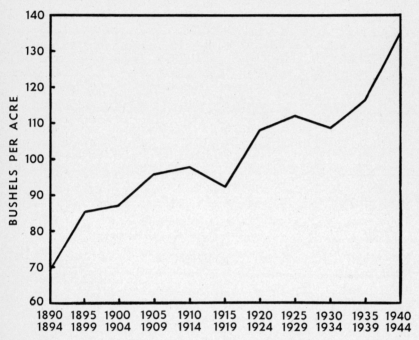

Graph II. Average yield of potatoes in the United States by 5-year periods, 1890–1944.

Trends in Production

With continually increasing labor costs and the availability of more and better machinery, fewer farmers are growing potatoes, and the total acreage is decreasing. According to the *U.S. Census* (1945), potatoes were harvested for home use or for sale from 21 per cent fewer farms in 1944 than in 1939. At the same time, the total acreage decreased about 4 per cent. This means that the average acreage per farm increased from 1.00 to 1.23 acres and that the trend is toward larger acreage units per farm. Heavy and expensive potato machinery, such as multiple-row planters, sprayers, diggers, and combines, do not lend themselves well to small fields and small acreages. With better transportation facilities, it is also more feasible than ever before to grow potatoes farther from home and market.

Commercial growers therefore are searching out the best potato soils and abandoning those less well adapted. Royston (1946), by comparing acreages in the sixteen high-, sixteen medium-, and sixteen low-yielding states over recent years has shown that there has been a definite shift from the low- to the high-yielding areas.

TABLE 5. ACREAGE, PRODUCTION, YIELD PER ACRE, AND PER-CENTAGE OF TOTAL U.S. ACREAGE OF FIFTEEN LEADING POTATO STATES ACCORDING TO *AGRICULTURAL STATISTICS,* U.S. DEPT. OF AGRICULTURE (AVERAGE 1941–1945).

State	(Thousands) Acres	Production (Thousand Bushels)	Yield per Acre (Bushels)	Per Cent of Total U.S. Acreage
Maine	183	52,703	288	6.3
Idaho	163	36,966	227	5.6
California	91	28,375	312	3.2
New York	191	28,082	147	6.6
North Dakota	156	19,921	128	5.4
Pennsylvania	162	19,870	123	5.6
Michigan	183	19,439	106	6.3
Minnesota	200	18,477	92	6.9
Colorado	83	17,443	210	2.9
Wisconsin	153	12,960	85	5.3
Nebraska	76	11,012	145	2.6
New Jersey	65	10,656	164	2.2
North Carolina	88	8,877	101	3.0
Ohio	79	8,257	105	2.7
Virginia	73	7,638	105	2.5
United States	2,899	399,871	138	100.0

Record Yields

Potato yields very much above average are usually obtained by a combination of good seed, abundant fertilizer, good soil, good weather, close planting, and thorough weed and pest control. Record yields are usually made on a measured acre or less and under conditions which cannot be considered altogether practical or economical.

All of the so-called record yields made in this country were made with benefit of irrigation. The author has fairly well-authenticated reports of six different yields of 1000 bushels or more to the acre, the highest being 1188 bushels made by R. C. Zuckerman of Stockton, California, in 1947. Without irrigation, yields of more than 700, 852, and 901 bushels to the acre at Glen Head, New York, Limestone, Maine, and Steveston, British Columbia, respectively, are recorded. A yield of 1188 bushels represents 2.54 pounds per plant for 28,000 plants in rows 28 inches apart, with plants 8 inches apart.

Geography of Production

The importance of potato production in any given state or region is dependent on one or more such factors as climate, soil, nearness to market, and competing enterprises. Of these factors, climate is most important. Profitable yields are not possible except where the mean growing-season temperature is between 60° and 70° F. and rainfall totals at least 15 inches, well distributed over a period of 3½ to 4 months. An inch of water each week, either as rainfall or irrigation water, is considered ideal. The Atlantic Seaboard states and most of those east of the Mississippi River have sufficient rainfall—sometimes too much for good yields. The low average yield of potatoes in Minnesota, Wisconsin, North Dakota, and other parts of the Red River Valley, and in most of the Great Plains area not irrigated is due to insufficient rainfall. However, the mean temperature in these three states is favorable. The fame of Aroostook County, Maine, is due mainly to its far north, cool climate and ideal potato soil. Colorado has a high elevation, and much of its crop is irrigated with water supplied from mountain snow. Idaho's famous baking potatoes are grown at a high elevation in a very friable lava-ash soil, under irrigation. The high yields of White Rose potatoes grown in Kern County, California, are obtained under irrigation in the foothills of the Sierra Nevada Mountains during the cool season. The famous Long Island potato region of New York and the region of Monmouth County, New Jersey, owe their prominence to the tempering influence of the Atlantic, to an ideal soil, and to their nearness to the world's best markets. Potatoes are an important crop in Virginia, North Carolina, Florida, Alabama, Louisiana, and Texas largely because they are grown during the season when the late crop of the north is off the market and prices are relatively high. Although yields in the South are not high, they are favored by the fact that the crop is grown during the coolest season of the year.

In a few regions where climate, soil, and market outlets are favorable for potato production, the industry is limited by competition with other farm enterprises. Such is the case in the intensive fruit-production belts of New York, Michigan, Oregon, and Washington. Competition for labor at spraying and harvest time interferes with care of the potato crop. This is equally true of the sugar beet industry of the West. Although the dairy industry offers some labor competition—and one seldom sees both enterprises extensively developed on the same farm—it is not a serious drawback to potato production. A limited dairy or poultry enterprise combined with potato growing provides the advantage of more efficient year-round labor than is otherwise possible. This combination, however, requires a fairly long crop rotation, which may or may not be advantageous to the potato enterprise.

REFERENCES

Agricultural Statistics. Washington, D.C.: U.S. Dept. Agr., 1946.

Balls, Edward K. Central and South American potatoes for the improvement of European and North American stocks. Eighth American Scientific Congress Proc., 3 (Biological Sciences), 143–147, 1940. Washington, D.C.: Dept. of State, 1942.

Royston, Reginald. Shifts in potato acreages and yields. Mimeographed address. Bur. Agr. Econ., U.S. Dept. Agr., November, 1946.

United States Census of Agriculture, 1945. Washington, D.C.: Bureau of the Census. Dept. Commerce.

CHAPTER 2

Botany and Plant Development

T O BE A STUDENT of the potato and to understand the response of the potato plant to its environment requires that one be familiar with its botany, anatomy, composition, and ontogeny. Although all of these characteristics vary with such factors as variety, inheritance, climate, soil, maturity, physiological age, nutritional status, relative freedom from disease, and storage, each of them is sufficiently stable to allow proximate description. The potato breeder should be familiar with the flower structure with which he effects the cross pollination, with blossoming habits of the plant, and with the genetic constitution of the parental material. The plant pathologist should know the gross morphology of the entire plant and the normal response of the plant to temperature and moisture if he is to predict and control the invasion of parasitic organisms to which the potato is subject. So, too, the housewife who buys and prepares potatoes for the table could better judge culinary quality if she were familiar with those external and internal tuber characters which denote maturity, quantity of starch, mealiness, dryness, tendency to slough when boiled, adaptability for baking, or perhaps even the tendency to darken after cooking. Certainly the potato grower who well knows the nature and habits of the potato plant under normal conditions of growth and storage is best able to safeguard his crop against those conditions of environment which cut down his yield and his income. This is especially true because the potato is rather sensitive to its environment during growth and rather perishable during storage.

Botanical Classification

The potato is the most important member of the *Solanaceae* or nightshade family. This family of plants, according to Bailey (1917), is made up of "a group of temperate and tropical herbs, shrubs, and even trees comparatively poorly represented in temperate North America, of various horticultural adaptabilities comprising ornamental subjects and also the potato, tomato, eggplant, ground cherry or physalis, red pepper or capsicum, also medicinal plants." Members of the *Solanaceae* have leaves borne alternate, blossoms in the leaf axils or on the leaf petioles or on the main stem, corolla bell-shaped and five-lobed, stamens five in number and inserted on the throat of the corolla, with ovary usually two-loculed. Bailey and Bailey (1941) list and describe about fifty species of the genus *Solanum* of which the most important is *S. tuberosum,* the species most widely cultivated throughout North America. Although the *Solanaceae* group of plants is found in abundance throughout the world, relatively few are of economic importance. Of these few, the cultivated eggplant *S. melongena* is the only other important food plant belonging to the same genus as the potato. Relatively few species of *Solanum* develop underground tubers, and among these none produces tubers as large as *S. tuberosum,* the potato of commerce.

Gross Morphology

The potato is a succulent, herbaceous, annual plant which, under favorable growth conditions, blossoms and develops underground tubers at the terminus of stolons or rhizomes. Characteristic of monocotyledonous plants, its leaves are borne alternately on the stem above ground, its stolons alternately below ground. Although a majority of the roots arise in whorls at the nodes on the main stem, some roots develop along the internodes. Similarly, although most of the tubers are borne at the terminus of the stolon, some may form on stolon branches or even sessile to the main stolons as shown in figure 3. Both leaves and stolons arise in an alternate, rotate arrangement around the main stem. The plant is irregularly branched, the branches arising at the axils formed by the leaves and main stem. The number of main stems of each plant varies with the number of eyes on the seed piece, these in turn varying with the size of the seed piece. Instead of being propagated from true seed, the potato is usually carried over from year to year by means of asexually propagated seed pieces or cut portions of the tuber, one of which is shown in figure 3. At maximum vegetative development, the potato plant normally reaches a height of 2 to 3 feet, although its sprawling habit may show an over-all length of stems, sometimes

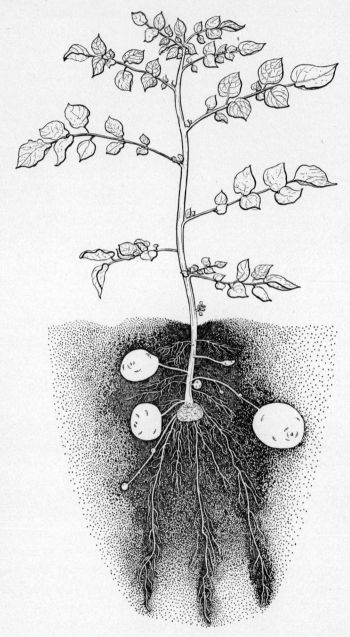

Fig. 3. Immature potato plant, about 10 weeks after planting. Note alternate rotate arrangement of leaves, new tubers borne terminally, sessile, and on stolon branches, main feeding roots, and old seed piece.

reaching as much as 6 feet in length on muck and peat soils. The root system is confined mostly to the upper 8 inches of soil, but the main roots may reach a lateral spread of 3 feet and some of them penetrate to a depth of 3 feet, depending on depth of the water table and character of the subsoil. The ratio of tuber to top at maximum development varies with variety but is approximately 2 to 1; at the same stage the ratio of root to top is 1 to 20 on the dry-matter basis.

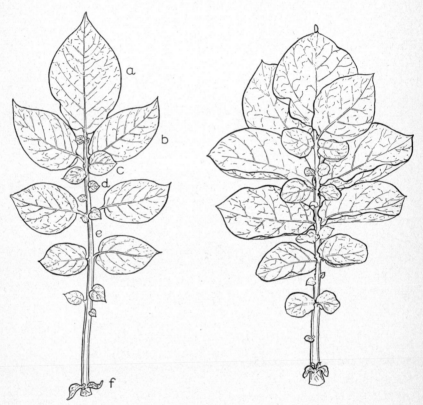

Fig. 4. Potato leaf types. *Left,* open type: (a) terminal leaflet, (b) primary leaflet, (c) secondary leaflet, (d) tertiary leaflet, (e) midrib, (f) stipule or leafy bract. *Right,* compact type.

The potato stem is roughly angular, with three to four sides, the diameter varying from 1/2 to 1 1/4 inches. As a characteristic of some varieties, the stem is distinctly winged, the wings being crinkled or straight. Other varieties, notably the Burbank and Russet Burbank, have small stems nearly round in cross section and with little or no winged character. Both types of stems are illustrated in figure 5. Internally the stem is solid, but inside the vascular ring the tissue is distinctly pithy, especially early in the growth period.

The potato leaf is compound and consists of a large terminal leaflet subtended by three to five pairs of leaflets borne laterally along a well-defined mid-rib. Each pair of leaflets decreases in size toward the base of the leaf and is sub-tended by one or two pairs of secondary or tertiary leaflets each similarly de-creasing in size. Varieties differ distinctly in leaf char-acters, some being open, others compact, depending on whether the leaflets are close together, overlapping, or widely spaced along the midrib. Similarly varieties differ according to the shape, size, and greenness of the leaflets. Two distinct types of potato leaves are shown in figure 4.

Flowers on the potato plant are of cymose forma-tion and open over a period of several days. Some va-rieties blossom more than others and the amount of

Fig. 5. Types of potato stems.
Left: winged. *Right:* round.

bloom varies with the season. Cool, humid weather favors the development of blossoms, and, for this reason, plants grown in Northern Maine, Minnesota, Michigan, and New York bloom more profusely than elsewhere in the United States. Dry, hot weather at blossoming time usually causes the flower buds to dehisce be-fore opening. Blossom color varies from white through various shades of pink to purple, the majority of present-day varieties hav-ing lavender blossoms. This is an important varietal character as shown in Chapter 8. The blossom stalk is most commonly borne in the axil of the leaf and main stem but sometimes on the leaf petiole, and sometimes on the main stem. Attempts have been made to classify varieties on the basis of position of the blossom stalk, but, because the character is not constant, such attempts are not very successful. The bell-shaped corolla is five-lobed, with five stamens borne on the corolla tube and converging around a single pistil. The stamens bear erect anthers which shed pollen from a large terminal

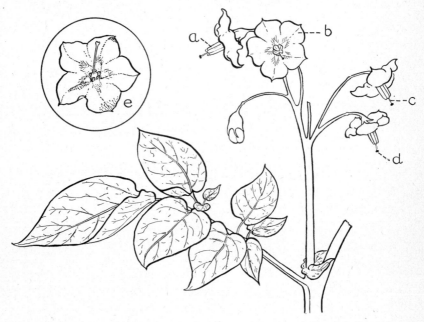

Fig. 6. Potato flower cluster: (a) stamen or anther sac, (b) 5-lobed corolla, (c) style, (d) stigma, (e) emasculated flower showing exposed ovary.

pore. Many of the varieties originated during the late nineteenth century produced very little and often sterile pollen. Most of our present-day varieties produce viable pollen profusely. Also there is less self-sterility among the newer varieties than among the older ones. The theory that senility is a cause of failure to blossom and fruit is now largely discredited. Wind and insects play only a very minor role in pollination of potato flowers. A typical cluster of potato blossoms together with an emasculated flower is shown in figure 6.

The true fruit or seed ball is similar to a small green tomato and

usually ranges from ¾ to 1¼ inches in diameter. Within the seed
ball are both pulp and placenta, the latter usually containing many
flattened-ovate-shaped seeds. The fruits of most of our newer
varieties contain viable seeds. This is especially true of the varieties
Katahdin, Chippewa, Houma, and Sebago. Some of the older varieties, such as Rural and Russet Rural, produce fruits sparsely and,
when they do, the fruits are usually parthenocarpic. A truss of

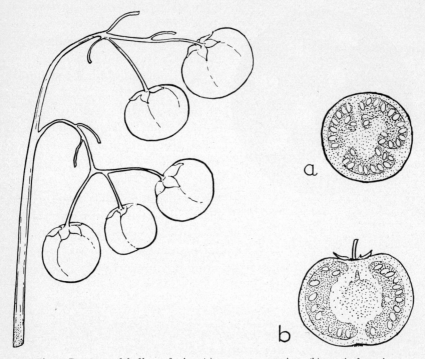

Fig. 7. Potato seed balls or fruits: (a) transverse section, (b) vertical section.

potato seed balls and both vertical and transverse sections of an
enlarged fruit are illustrated in figure 7. A group of potato seeds
considerably enlarged is shown in figure 8.

The potato tuber is an enlarged portion of the underground stem,
rhizome, or stolon. It represents mostly stored or surplus carbohydrate material not used by the plant for vegetative growth, fruiting, and other essential life processes. Although most tubers arise
at the terminus of the stolon, they sometimes are formed on stolon
branches and even sessile to or continuous with the main stolon
(see figure 3). The tuber is structurally a stem and consists of all

homologous parts common to woody and herbaceous stems. Its surface carries dormant axillary buds in groups of usually three to five, each group subtended by a leaf scar. This leaf scar, commonly called the eyebrow, together with its group of dormant buds, constitute the "eye." The eyes of the tuber have a definite rotate alternate distribution from the stem end to the apical bud at the distal end of the tuber. Every eye "looks" toward the apical bud. The

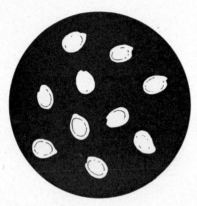

majority of the eyes are on the upper surface of the tuber, indicating the phototropic tendency of the eyes to develop in the direction of light. The apical bud is normally the one to develop first and to dominate the growth of all other buds on the tuber. This phenomenon is called apical dominance. Just as the apical bud of the tuber is dominant over all other eyes or buds, so the central bud in each eye is normally dominant over the other buds in the same eye. Destruction of the apical buds usually results in stem growth of some of the other eyes and so increases the number of stems or stalks arising from a single tuber or seed piece.

Fig. 8. Potato seeds enlarged about 10 times. Note flat ovate shape.

Ontogeny and Plant Development

A knowledge of the life history of the potato plant from planting of the seed piece or mother tuber to maturity is basic to successful production. It better enables the grower to adjust his cultural and seed handling practices to such habits of the plant as are conducive to maximum yield. The pursuit of such knowledge is a major function of most potato research.

The seasonal life history of the potato plant may well be divided into three periods: (1) rapid plant growth, during which every seed and cultural practice should be designed to promote vigorous, healthy development of the plant, (2) plant maintenance and rapid tuber development, and (3) plant decline during which the plant is maturing and the tubers are enlarging at a decreasing rate. During the period of plant maintenance, the aim should be to protect the plant from disease and insect pests and to preserve the root system in order that the plant may most fully function in the synthesis of the carbohydrates necessary for tuber development. Environmental or cultural factors which tend to stimulate plant growth during this second period may not increase yields if by so doing all the carbohydrates are used in growth and respiration.

The life span of the potato plant from planting to maturity ranges from about 80 days to 150 days, depending on the variety. In the regions of highest average yields, the number of days available between planting and killing frost is usually not over 120 days. In such regions the high yield is due to favorable temperature and is obtained in spite of the limited growing season. To obtain maximum yields, the aim should be to utilize the longest growth period available and not to harvest before the plant is mature. This is often neither possible nor feasible because of an early killing frost, and because with large acreages the harvest must begin before danger of freezing weather.

To establish and define our terminology, it is well first to define tuberization or tuber set, as distinct from tuber development as these terms will be used in this chapter. Tuberization is the initiation of tubers by the enlargement of the terminus of the underground stolon. By the author's usage of the term, tuber set refers to the number of tubers which form early in the life of the plant and should not be confounded with the number of tubers per plant at harvest time. Tuberization occurs normally about six weeks after planting, and when the plant is in the early bud stage. It occurs in response to conditions favoring the translocation and storage of surplus soluble carbohydrates above those used in growth and respiration of the plant. The absence of light around the underground stolon, temperature, and moisture are factors which most influence tuberization or tuber set. Artschwager (1924) has shown that at the time of tuberization a large proportion of the stolon tip is cortical tissue, but as the tuber enlarges the ratio of pith or parenchyma tissue to cortical tissue increases. Growth is mainly by cell division, most rapid in the medulla and less so in the cortex. Some idea of the anatomy and developmental changes from tuberization to the mature tuber can be obtained from figures 9 and 10.

Clark (1921) working with the Rural New Yorker No. 2 variety at Greeley, Colorado, counted the number of tubers per plant beginning at weekly intervals soon after the period of tuber formation and up to the time the plants were killed by frost. The range of growth period was from 64 to 127 days. He found very little increase in tuber set after the blossom stage and concluded that small tubers at harvest time are the result of uneven growth rate rather than a late "set." This means that most small potatoes are of the same physiological age as the large ones. He found evidence that many of the small tubers originally formed decomposed or were resorbed into the plant.

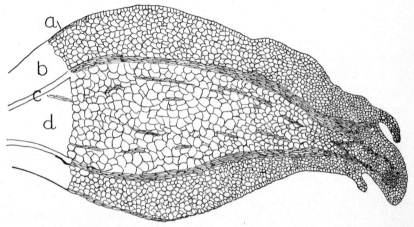

Fig. 9. Longitudinal section through tip of stolon at time of tuberization (note high proportion of cortical tissue): (a) epidermal cells, (b) cortex, (c) vascular ring, mainly xylem tissue, (d) medulla, mainly thin-walled parenchyma tissue. (After Dutt in Jones and Rosa, *Truck Crop Plants*.)

Hardenburg (1923), also working with the Rural variety, studied the effect of temperature and soil moisture on tuber set in greenhouse soil cultures. In this study the plants were still green and very immature when harvested after a period of 14 weeks from the time of planting. Plants were thinned to one stalk to eliminate the factor of competition due to multiple sprouting. The plants were grown under two fairly constant temperatures, a mean of 59.5° F. in the cool greenhouse, and a mean of 68.6° F. in the warm house. Three levels of soil moisture were maintained under each temperature by regular periods of watering to constant weight, namely 17.7 per cent, 20.5 per cent, and 23.2 per cent wet basis. The numbers of tubers actually set per plant in the cool and the warm house were

24.6 and 55.8 respectively. The weight of tubers per plant in the cool house, however, was nearly double that in the warm house. The number and weight of stolons were much greater on the plants grown at the higher temperature. This indicates that high temperature encourages a large set and a low yield of tubers and that tuber set and yield are in inverse relationship. As for the influence of soil moisture on tuber set, this varied with temperature. In the cool greenhouse the relationship was inverse, while in the warm house it was direct. In the cool house the tuber set in the dry soil was nearly double that in the wet soil. Regardless of temperature, total weight of tubers per plant was proportionate to soil moisture. The conclusions from this 2-year experiment are that a relatively low temperature favors a low tuber set and, because of less competition between tubers, a higher yield than does a high temperature. Also, under a favorably low temperature, soil moisture below the optimum level results in a larger tuber set and a correspondingly lower yield than does a wetter soil. As between the two factors temperature and soil moisture, temperature appears to have the greater influence on both tuber set and yield.

Bushnell (1925) at the Minnesota Experiment Station grew potato plants in glass temperature-controlled chambers, maintaining the temperatures at 20°, 23°, 26°, and 29° C. Although he did not report results of tuber set, the average weights of tubers in grams per plant for these temperatures were 20.9, 5.0, 1.6, and 0.0 respectively. This is further evidence that even though high temperature increases the set of tubers, when it exceeds 20° C. or 68° F., it accelerates the respiration rate and possibly also the growth rate of the plant so much that no surplus of carbohydrate is available for tuber development, and no tubers form. Inexperienced growers sometimes think that blossoming of the plant is necessary for good yields, or that if few or no blossoms appear the yield will be low. This relationship does not necessarily hold. Nevertheless hot, dry conditions during the period of blossoming and tuberization obviously would increase the premature abscission of blossom buds and at the same time favor a heavy tuber set and a correspondingly low yield.

Bartholdi (1942) studied the influence of flowering and fruiting on vegetative growth and tuber yield at two locations in northern Minnesota. He found that fruit formation and tuber production are concurrent processes. By removing flowers from certain plants and fruits from others for comparison with normal plants, he found that "yields were reduced significantly on both fruiting and flowering plants of all varieties as compared to non-flowering, non-fruiting plants." Decrease in yield appeared to be related to the number of flowers and fruits formed.

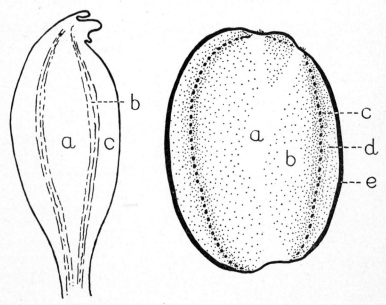

Fig. 10. *Left,* embryonic tuber at time of tuberization or swelling of terminus of stolon: (a) medullary tissue, (b) vascular ring, (c) cortex. *Right,* transverse section of mature tuber showing density of starch and dry matter in various areas: (a) inner medulla, (b) outer medulla, (c) vascular ring, (d) cortex, (e) epidermis.

Anatomy and Composition of the Tuber

A longitudinal, transverse section of a potato tuber, such as that illustrated in figure 11 shows it to be composed, from surface to central axis, of a periderm, cortex, vascular ring, outer medulla, and inner medulla or pith. Before tuberization, the cortical tissue composes about 50 per cent of the entire volume, whereas at maturity this ratio is much smaller. The outer periderm or epidermis is mostly cork tissue acting as a protective layer and is formed from the inner periderm or endodermis. The latter may or may not carry the pigment which gives certain varieties their characteristic skin color. The inner medulla or pith is the central axis of the tuber and forms a continuous connection from the stem end to the apical bud and to the buds in each of the eyes. Cells of the periderm are mostly brick-shaped, while those of the cortex and the mullary areas are polyhedral, usually five-sided. Except in the endodermis and some of the xylem tissue throughout the tuber, the cells are thin-walled. Density of starch is normally greatest in the tissue on

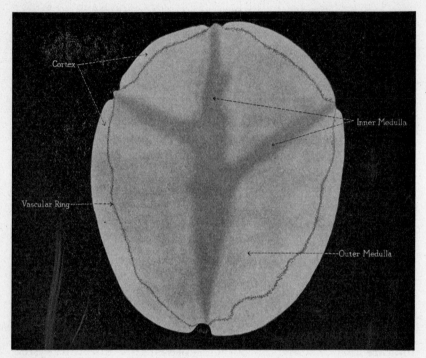

Fig. *11*. Anatomy of potato tuber. Note dark, watery, inner medulla or pith branching to each eye.

either side of the vascular ring. The greater part of the protein and minerals is concentrated in the cortex. Growth of the tuber is mainly by cell division and deposition of soluble carbohydrates in the parenchyma tissue.

The production of dry matter in the entire plant continues to increase up to maturity or about 4 months from planting date. This increase is usually most rapid during the second month, as shown in table 6, adapted from the data of Ramsey and Robertson (1917). Those data indicate that, during the growth period, the ratio of

tuber to top weight increases to about 2 to 1 while the ratio of root
to top weight decreases to about 1 to 20.

TABLE 6. TOTAL DRY MATTER AT VARIOUS DATES AFTER
PLANTING (GRAMS PER PLANT).*

Date Dug	Stem	Tubers	Roots	Total	Tuber-Top Ratio	Root-Top Ratio
Jan. 29	49.4	3.4	6.3	59.1	0.07	0.13
Feb. 23	158.9	147.1	14.3	320.3	0.93	0.09
Mar. 26	219.5	352.4	15.3	587.2	1.60	0.07
Apr. 30	213.0	423.4	10.7	647.1	1.99	0.05

* Potatoes planted December 27.

Lampitt and Goldenberg (1940) state that the chemical composition of the potato tuber varies with the variety, age, conditions of
growth, and perhaps other factors. Also, because the composition
of the cortex is different from that of the medullary, results of
analyses vary depending on whether peeled or unpeeled tubers are
used. These authors state that averages of many analyses show the
percentage composition of the raw tuber to be as follows: water
72.1 to 80.0, dry solids 23.0, protein 2.0, starch 12.4 to 17.8, total
nitrogen 1.7 to 2.6, sugars 0.2 to 6.8, ash 0.96, fat 0.056 to 0.11, and
crude fiber 0.4 to 1.0. Artschwager states that sugar is usually not
present in the mature tuber except when it is very young and again
just before it begins to sprout. Lampitt and Goldenberg further
indicate that the free amino acids present are histidine, lysine,
arginine, and tyrosine. Tuberin, a globulin, constitutes 48 to 67
per cent of the total nitrogen. The acids present are oxalic, citric,
malic, succinic, and tartaric. The enzymes present are tyrosinase,
peroxidase, dehydrase, catalase, phosphorylase, and amylase. Solanin, from which the potato family is named, is an alkaloid glu-
coside present 20 to 90 milligrams per kilogram of fresh tuber.
According to Artschwager (1924), solanin is found in large quantities in the young tuber, but in the mature tuber only in the region
of the buds. Apparently it functions in the metabolism of the growing plant, because it disappears from the base of the tuber as it
enters the growing sprout. If germination is retarded in the spring,

solanin may accumulate in such quantity as to be poisonous to man. For this reason, sunburned or green-sprouted tubers, or sprouts removed from stored tubers, should not be eaten or fed to livestock in large amounts.

A good source of information on the mineral content of the ash of the edible portion of the potato tuber is furnished by Esselen, Lyons, and Fellers (1942). The data are compiled in table 7.

TABLE 7. MINERAL CONTENT OF THE EDIBLE PORTION OF THE POTATO (A BREAKDOWN OF THE ASH CONSTITUENT).

Mineral	Per Cent	Mineral	Per Cent
Potassium	0.496	Aluminum	0.00097
Phosphorus	0.053	Zinc	0.0004
Chlorine	0.035	Manganese	0.00017
Sulfur	0.029	Copper	0.00016
Magnesium	0.027	Nickel	Trace
Sodium	0.024	Cobalt	Trace
Calcium	0.013	Barium	Trace
Iron	0.0011	Iodine	Trace

On the basis of these analyses, the potato is said to be a good source of potassium, phosphorus, and iron, a poor source of calcium. It rates high as an energy food, as it furnishes about 385 calories per pound. It also is desirable as a source of food useful in neutralizing excess acidity, as its approximate potential reserve alkalinity is 9 cc. alkali per 100 grams of raw tuber. These same authors rate the potato as a source of vitamins as follows: vitamin A, very low and a poor source; vitamin B_1 (thiamin), 8 to 60 international units, medium to low; vitamin B_2 (riboflavin), 0.012 mg., low; vitamin C (ascorbic acid), 3.1 to 33 mg., high; vitamin D, none. These figures show that the potato is a good source of vitamin C but does not rate high in any of the others.

The composition of the potato tuber changes gradually during its developmental period from tuberization to maturity. This was well shown by Appleman and Miller (1926) who analyzed Cobbler potatoes harvested at weekly intervals from June 17 to August 27. The changes in composition are shown in table 8.

According to these analyses, as the tuber approaches maturity,

TABLE 8. SEASONAL CHANGES IN COMPOSITION OF POTATO
TUBER (PERCENTAGE COMPOSITION OF RAW TUBERS).

Date Dug	Water	Ash	Crude Fiber	Protein	Total Sugars	Starch	Plant Stage
June 17	84	0.91	0.34	1.77	1.03	10.6	Full bloom
June 24	83	0.91	0.30	1.85	1.03	11.5	Bloom gone
July 8	81	0.91	0.32	1.82	0.68	13.8	Leaves dying
July 15	79	1.00	0.31	2.23	0.30	15.0	Leaves 80% dead
July 22	80	1.02	0.31	2.24	0.19	14.3	Leaves all dead
August 27	81	1.03	0.32	2.17	0.26	13.6	Stems dead

there is a slight increase in total dry matter, an increase in ash, protein, and starch, and a decrease in water and total sugars. Although most of the sugars are nonsaccharine, these figures may explain why new potatoes sometimes taste sweeter than old. Also they indicate that the total nutritive value, as well as the yield of potatoes, increases up to complete maturity.

REFERENCES

Appleman, C. O., and E. V. Miller. A chemical and physiological study of maturity in potatoes. Jour. Agr. Research 33, No. 6, 1926.

Artschwager, Ernst. Studies on the potato tuber. Jour. Agr. Research 27, No. 11, 1924.

Bailey, L. H. The standard cyclopedia of horticulture, VI. New York: The Macmillan Company, 1917.

Bailey, L. H., and Ethel Zoe Bailey. Hortus Second. New York: The Macmillan Company, 1941.

Bartholdi, W. L. Influence of flowering and fruiting upon vegetative growth and tuber yield in the potato. Minn. Agr. Exp. Sta. Tech. Bul. 150, 1942.

Bushnell, John. The relation of temperature to growth and respiration in the potato plant. Minn. Agr. Exp. Sta. Tech. Bul. 34, 1925.

Clark, Charles F. Development of tubers in the potato. U.S. Dept. Agr. Bul. 958, 1921.

Esselen, William B., Jr., Mary E. Lyons, and Carl R. Fellers. The composition and nutritive value of potatoes with special emphasis on vitamin C. Mass. Agr. Exp. Sta. Bul. 390, 1942.

Hardenburg, E. V. Ecological factors affecting tuber-set in potatoes. Potato Assn. of Amer. Proc., 1923.

Jones, H. A., and J. T. Rosa, Jr. Truck crop plants. New York: McGraw-Hill Book Company, Inc., 1928.

Lampitt, L. H., and N. Goldenberg. Potato as food: Composition. Chemistry and Industry 59, 1940.

Ramsey, J. T., and W. C. Robertson. The composition of the potato plant at various stages of development. Jour. Dept. Agr. of Victoria (Australia) 15, No. 2, 1917.

CHAPTER 3

Climatic and Soil Relationships

WEATHER is the most important single factor influencing the yield of potatoes. Limitations on acreage, fertilizer, spray materials, and equipment imposed by government or other agencies from year to year may or may not be effective depending on whether the weather throughout the growing season is favorable. Weather more than anything else determines size of crop, and size of crop, together with the general price level, in a free market, determines the farm price of potatoes. Weather, like soil, is extremely complex and cannot be defined as simply a combination of temperature and rainfall at any given moment. So far as its effect on the yield and quality of potatoes is concerned, weather involves not only total rainfall and mean growing season temperature but also rainfall distribution, fluctuation and extremes of temperature, length of growing season, killing frost dates, wind velocity, relative humidity, total sunshine, and quality and intensity of light. Furthermore, there is a critical period in the ontogeny of the plant during which the elements of weather are more influential on final crop results than at other times. This critical period usually occurs about six weeks after date of planting, or when the plant reaches its early bud and tuber-setting stage. For most of the northern states, the weather in July is more influential on the yield of potatoes than that of any other month of the growing season. It is shown in Chapter 2 how temperature and soil moisture affect tuber set and this, in turn, the final yield.

Temperature

The potato is a cool-weather crop. It has yielded best in the northern and western part of the United States where the mean annual temperature is between 40° and 50° F., and where the mean temperature of July is not over 70° F. Highest yields are obtained in Maine and the central Rocky Mountain states where the mean annual temperature is below 45° F., and where the mean of the warmest month is not far from 65° F. Smith (1916) of the United States Weather Bureau studied the relation of mean monthly temperature and of monthly rainfall to the average yield of potatoes during the months of June, July, August, and September in Ohio,

Fig. 12. Potato plants grown in cool greenhouse (59° F.). Note short, stocky plants with broad leaflets.

Michigan, and New Jersey. The results indicated that July temperature for these states is the most important single weather factor. This relationship for the 55-year period, 1860 to 1914, in Ohio is shown in table 9.

An analysis of table 9 makes it appear that temperature is more influential on yield than is moisture, that the best combination of weather in Ohio is a relatively cool and wet season, that the probability of a yield above normal in such a season is about 80 per cent, and that rainfall is often a limiting factor. The influence of temperature without regard to rainfall for this same period in Ohio is indicated in table 10.

TABLE 9. RELATION OF JULY WEATHER TO THE YIELD OF POTA-
TOES IN OHIO FOR THE 55-YEAR PERIOD 1860–1914.

July Weather	No. of Years	No. of Years When Yield Was:		Probability of Yield above Normal in Per Cent
		Above Normal	Below Normal	
Warm and wet	13	3	10	23
Warm and dry	14	4	10	29
Cool and dry	14	7	7	50
Cool and wet	14	11	3	80

These data indicate that for every degree rise in mean July temperature, the average yield of potatoes decreased four bushels to
the acre. A similar study by Smith for New Jersey for the 30-year
period, 1885–1915, showed that there were 11 years during which
the July temperature averaged one degree or more above normal.
The average yield for these years was 12 bushels per acre below
normal. For the 12 years when the July mean temperature averaged
one degree or more below normal, the average yield was 11 bushels
per acre above normal. Fox (1918) determined the coefficient of
correlation (r) for monthly mean temperature and total monthly
rainfall and average yield of potatoes in New York for the 26-
year period, 1890–1915. The coefficient for July temperature was
–0.35 and for July rainfall was –0.45. The values for July were
much higher than for the other months of the growing season, again
indicating that July weather is more influential on yield than that

TABLE 10. RELATION OF JULY MEAN TEMPERATURE TO THE
YIELD OF POTATOES IN OHIO FOR THE PERIOD 1860–1914.

Temperature in Degrees F.			No. of Years	Average Yield per Acre (Bushels)	
Variation	Mean	Increase		Average	Decrease
Below 72.6	71.5	—	16	86.6	—
72.6–73.5	73.1	1.6	13	80.0	–6.6
73.6–74.5	74.1	1.0	11	76.5	–3.5
Above 74.5	76.3	2.2	15	67.7	–8.8

of the other months. Fox's results checked with those of Smith's except that the relation of July rainfall to yield was negative instead of positive. This means that rainfall in July in New York is usually

Fig. 13. Potato plants grown in warm greenhouse (68° F.). Note tall spindly plants with leaflets smaller and narrower than in the same variety shown in figure 12.

not a limiting factor. On the contrary, July rainfall in New York exceeds that of any other month normally, and when late blight is found in potato fields as early as this it often reaches endemic proportions by fall, causing a reduction in yield.

Rainfall

The potato is naturally adapted to humid regions. The plant is highly succulent, the mature tuber being nearly 80 per cent water. Its water requirement, the average weight of available water required for each pound of dry matter produced, approximates 400 pounds. For steady growth and maximum yield, rainfall or its equivalent in irrigation water should be so distributed as to provide the growing plant with about one acre inch of water each week. This adds to a growing season total of 15 to 17 inches of rain. Poor rainfall distribution affects both plant and tuber. Dry, hot weather usually results in smaller, narrower, more spoon-shaped leaflets than

Fig. 14. Rural variety grown at different levels of soil moisture. *Left:* high moisture (25 per cent). *Right:* low moisture (16 per cent).

normal. Rainy weather following periods of drought and a check in growth generally causes second-growth or knobby tubers in varieties subject to this defect. This is especially true of such varieties as Cobbler, Early Ohio, Burbank, Russet Burbank, and Rural. It is for this reason that late rains following dry weather, while they may cause a resumption in tuber development, often do not result in an increase in marketable yield.

In such well-known potato-growing areas as the Red River Valley of the Dakotas, and Minnesota, Wisconsin, Nebraska, and the Kaw Valley of Kansas, potato yields are relatively low because of a lack of sufficient rainfall. In other semiarid potato areas, such as Colorado, Wyoming, southern Idaho, Montana, and Kern County, California, high average yields are obtained by the use of irrigation water. This water may derive from irrigation reservoirs, from the Snake River as in Idaho, from mountain snows as in Colorado and Montana, or from drilled wells as in Southern California.

Irrigation

As early as 1929, nearly 60 per cent of the total potato acreage grown in the twelve western states was irrigated. Since then, government dam projects and other sources of water have increased the proportion of acreage irrigated. States in which the highest proportion of the total acreage is irrigated are Utah, California, Idaho, Colorado, and Nevada. In the census year 1929, the average yield from the unirrigated acreage was 79.7 bushels, from the irrigated acreage in the same states 191.7 bushels to the acre.

The most common method of irrigation is to run water from head ditches through furrows between the rows of potatoes. During part or all of the season the water may be applied in only every other furrow. Depending on soil type and seasonal rainfall, the number of irrigations may vary from 2 to as many as 10, 4 to 6 being most common. Experience has indicated that light applications applied often are more effective than heavy applications applied less often. Although water should be applied before the plants wilt, growers commonly use the color of the plants as an indicator, a dark blue-green color indicating the need for water. In porous soils subject to leaching, the furrows are made narrower and shallower than in heavier soils. The aim should be to keep the level of the water table below the level of the seed piece or the developing tubers; otherwise the tubers may become waterlogged and affected with enlarged lenticels. Where the soil is especially dry early in the season, the land is sometimes flooded before plowing; after the land is furrowed and planted the crop is "irrigated up" to facilitate germination of the seed pieces.

Edmundson (1938) at the Greeley Station in Colorado studied the effect of time of irrigating on stolon growth, tuber set, and yield. Using both Rural New Yorker No. 2 and Bliss Triumph varieties, he compared early irrigation, in which water was applied throughout the season to keep the plants in good color and growing steadily, with late irrigation in which water was applied only after the plants showed dark green and had been checked in growth. During the seven years, 1929–1935, the range in dates of the first applications,

as between early and late irrigation, varied from 14 to 34 days. Time
of irrigation had little effect on the number of stolons per plant,
but the early watering produced a more rapid growth and development of stolons than the late. Early irrigation lowered the soil temperature slightly through July and August, produced an earlier set
and a more rapid development of tubers, and, although it had little
effect on number of tubers per plant, it did increase the number of
large tubers.

Metzger (1938) states that "potatoes obtain nearly all their
moisture from the first 3 feet of soil; so when a soil is in need of irrigation it is useless to apply more than 3 to 6 inches in any one
application, as this is all the soil will hold." He also points out that
where plenty of water is available in Colorado, many growers over-
irrigate, with the result that yield is reduced and black scurf, worm
track, and bruising and skinning at harvest are increased. Irrigation should stop in time for the tubers to mature before harvest.

In scattered areas in the East and Middle West, many growers
use portable irrigation equipment, applying water only during
drought periods and getting their water supply from natural streams
or from drilled wells. Portable irrigation is a system by which water
pipe is moved successively across the field in sections. In these areas,
irrigation is economical and practical if an ample supply of water
is accessible and the acreage is large enough to justify the investment
in equipment. On Long Island the number of potato growers drill-
ing wells and installing portable equipment increases every year.

During the dry season of 1944, a potato grower in Wyoming
County in western New York irrigated 70 of his 117 acres with two
sets of portable equipment. His investment in each outfit including
pumps and pipe approximated $4000. Only two applications apply-
ing 1½ to 2 acre inches of water at each were made during a dry
2-week period. The yield from the irrigated acreage averaged 471
bushels, from the unirrigated 361 bushels to the acre. His cost of
operation and net returns from irrigation were figured as follows:

6 men—14 days at $5.00	$420.00
600 gallons gasoline at $0.20	120.00
Interest on investment, $8000 at 6%	480.00
Depreciation on equipment at 6¼%	500.00
Total cost per year	$1520.00

Cost per acre per application   10.86

Value of increased yield of unharvested
    crop, 110 bushels at $1.00   110.00
Total cost per acre   21.72
          Net gain per acre $ 88.28

Returns from irrigation as profitable as the above can be expected only when the water deficit is high, plants are free from disease, the fertility level is ample, and the stand of plants is good.

Light and Photoperiodism

Driver and Hawkes (1943) have published an excellent review of this subject, and much of the following discussion is adapted from their report.

The effect of light on growth and development of the potato plant is dependent on (1) intensity, (2) quality, and (3) duration of exposure. Effects of the first two of these are not so definitely established as the effects of duration of exposure. The effect of photoperiod may be overshadowed by the effect of temperature. Thus a very low temperature may encourage varieties to form tubers under longer photoperiods than those to which they are accustomed. With most species, a high temperature is antagonistic to tuber production and may largely nullify the beneficial effect of the short day.

Effect of Photoperiod on Vegetative Growth. Authors generally agree that a long day, particularly in the early growth period, acts to increase vegetative growth, stem elongation being most affected. Under a short day, plants have the largest terminal leaflets and greatest tendency to determinate growth, but decreasing light intensity may increase leaf size above that of plants grown in short days.

Effect of Photoperiod on Flowering and Fertilization. It is not well established that flowering and fruiting in the potato is a true function of photoperiod. Long day and strong light intensity do not markedly increase the number of flower primordia formed, but they do result in more fruit production because of less abortion and less flower-bud abscission.

Effect of Photoperiod on Stolon Formation. In general, long days encourage the formation of numerous long, branched stolons.

Werner (1934, 1940) got maximum stolon growth under long-day conditions which, combined with warm temperatures, also favored vegetative growth. However, the effect of photoperiod on stolon growth seems to vary depending on whether the species is normally adapted to long or short days.

Effect of Photoperiod on Tuberization. The formation of tubers in the potato is a function of the surplus carbohydrate material after the plant has used what is necessary for growth and respiration. All the evidence in literature indicates that shortening the daylight period to about 10 to 12 hours encourages the plant to devote a larger portion of the carbohydrates resulting from photosynthesis to the formation or growth of tubers and less to vegetative growth. Although short days are beneficial to tuber production and, per unit of plant weight, are more efficient producers of tubers than are long days, yet because of their greater vegetative bulk, long-day plants may give a greater final yield than short-day plants. Temperature, too, may upset the effect of photoperiod, a low temperature being more favorable to tuber production than a high one. Species and varieties differ considerably in their response to varying photoperiods, as reported by Garner and Allard (1923), Tincker (1925), Werner (1940), McClelland (1928), and Hackborth (1935). In general, the early-maturing varieties are favored by relatively long days, whereas late varieties are better adapted to short days during the period of tuber development. Miller and McGoldrick (1941) reported that tubers formed under short-day conditions were smoother than under long-day conditions, and Schick (1931) found that tuber shape was improved and tuber pigmentation decreased under short-day conditions.

Effect of Photoperiod on Maturity. Potato plants tend to mature earlier under short-day than under a long photoperiod. In fact, Garner and Allard (1923) found it possible by use of a long photoperiod to maintain vegetative growth almost indefinitely. To quote these workers, "It appears that progressive loss of power to grow as a result of decreasing day length, advances more rapidly than would be required from the decreased formation of carbohydrate as a controlling factor. It is necessary to conclude therefore that the duration of the light period exercises a regulatory action on the internal processes of the plant other than those which merely determine the total quantity of carbohydrate produced."

It is generally conceded that photoperiodic reaction is inherited, short-day type being dominant over long-day type. For this reason, it is difficult, if not impossible, to adapt foreign varieties grown under widely differing conditions of photoperiod to commercial production in the United States. Potato experiments started in the greenhouse at Ithaca, New York, during the winter season, usually result in poor yields of tubers and a low tuber-to-top ratio because the period of tuber development necessarily comes when the days are lengthening. Planted normally outdoors in May or early June at this latitude (42°), the potato plant enjoys a favorable photoperiod of long days for plant development and short days for tuber development and maturity.

Soil

Soils that generally produce the highest yield and the best quality of potatoes are friable, porous, well aerated, and well drained to a depth of at least 12 inches. Such soils are easily tilled, quick to warm up before planting, allow the development of good tuber shape, permit easy digging of the crop, and do not provide conditions favorable for the development of blight rot of the tubers. Extremely sandy soils are not suitable because they are not sufficiently retentive of ground water. Deep, well-drained, medium loams are preferred. Soils derived from organic material, if well drained, well decomposed, and adequately fertilized usually produce large yields of good-looking tubers. In choosing a farm, a field, or a soil for potatoes, soil texture, drainage, and soil reaction are of prime importance. Natural fertility and organic matter content are of less importance, because these factors can be adjusted or corrected at relatively little cost. On the other hand, it is costly, time consuming, and usually impossible to make a good soil out of one naturally poor. Potato tubers, roots, and stolons occupy a considerable volume of soil space and naturally require good soil aeration for proper development.

The sensitivity of the potato plant to soil aeration has been well demonstrated by Bushnell (1935) at the Ohio Experiment Station. Working with Wooster silt loam, a good general purpose soil, which had been in a 3-year rotation of potatoes, wheat, and clover for many years, it was found that the yield of potatoes had declined to a low and unprofitable level. This was obviously related to insufficient oxygen supply for the development of the underground parts of the plant. During the years 1929 to 1932 inclusive, by adding sand at an average rate of 5400 cubic feet to the acre, Bushnell was able to increase the yield of potatoes by over 25 per cent. This led him to study further the response of the potato plant to increased aeration. He provided the increased aeration by the use of both plain and perforated tile laid directly beneath the rows of potatoes. As a check, he dug trenches, refilled them, and planted seed directly above so as to provide conditions identical except for the tile aeration. The average total yield and the yield of large tubers for the years 1933 and 1934 for the three treatments are given in table 11.

TABLE 11. EFFECT OF SOIL AERATION, AS PROVIDED BY PLAIN AND PERFORATED TILE, ON YIELD OF POTATOES AT THE OHIO STATION.

Treatment	Average Yield per Acre 1933 and 1934 (Bushels)		Increase in Total Yield (Per Cent)
	Total	Large	
Check (no tile)	341.5	306.0	—
Plain tile	380.5	345.0	11.4
Perforated tile	410.0	378.4	7.8

Since the above differences are significant, and since the added aeration by perforated tile as compared to no tile at all gave an increased yield of about 70 bushels to the acre or 20 per cent, here is good evidence that soil aeration may well be the limiting factor to potato yields on heavy soil.

Examples of good potato soils well known for their high yields of good-quality crop are the Caribou silt loam and Washburn silt loam in Aroostook County, Maine, the Sassafras silt loam on Long Island, New York, and in New Jersey, the Bath gravelly loam in Steuben County, New York, and the lava ash soils of Southern Idaho. All of these are deep, well drained, not readily subject to puddling or poor aeration, quickly warmed, and distinctly acid in reaction.

Soil type influences the potato crop in a number of ways; among them are character of the skin and shape of tuber, composition of tuber, number of tubers per plant, yield, and the incidence of blight rot. Light, sandy, or gravelly soils yield tubers with rougher, more flaky skin than do heavy soils. Hardenburg (1926) studied the effect of soil type on tuber shape in Cobbler and Green Mountain varieties by growing these varieties on contrasting soil types on the same farm. Shape differences were expressed as L/W, the coefficient of elongation, and T/L, the coefficient of thickness, where L = length, W = width, and T = thickness. The results are shown in table 12.

TABLE 12. EFFECT OF SOIL TYPE ON SHAPE OF TUBER.

Variety	Soil Type	L/W	T/L
Cobbler	Peat	1.106	0.781
	Sandy loam	1.129	0.728
Green Mountain	Muck	1.391	0.562
	Heavy silt loam	1.357	0.572

In interpreting these results, the author states that the Cobbler is naturally a short, thick tuber and reached its most typical shape on the peat soil, while the Green Mountain, typically an elongated, flattened tuber, reached its most typical shape on the muck soil. He therefore concludes that the tubers of potato varieties attain their most typical shape on the most friable soils or those which offer least resistance.

In 1943 the author tested for specific gravity fourteen varieties grown from identical lots of seed, on both gravelly silt loam and muck soil. In ten of the fourteen varieties the specific gravity was higher for the upland-grown lot. Three of the other four varieties showed no difference. Similarly, the author found that potatoes grown in muck soil analyze a much higher percentage of nitrate nitrogen than the same strain and variety grown in upland soil. This difference between these two soil types is shown in table 13.

Probably the best report on the influence of soil type on number of harvested tubers per plant and yield is that of Clark (1921). Comparing three soil types at the potato station at Greeley, Colorado,

TABLE 13. RELATION OF SOIL NITRATE NITROGEN TO NITRATE NITROGEN CONTENT OF POTATO TUBER.

Soil Type and Variety	Soil Nitrates (p.p.m.)	Tuber Nitrates (p.p.m.)
Muck soil		
Cobbler	291	131
Green Mountain	235	147
White Rural	344	123
Silt loam soil		
Cobbler	65	15
Green Mountain	50	27
White Rural	63	18

he found that the lighter soil favored both yield and total number of tubers harvested. His results with two varieties are summarized in table 14.

TABLE 14. EFFECT OF SOIL TYPE ON NUMBER OF TUBERS PER PLANT AND YIELD.

Soil Type	Triumph		Rural	
	No. Tubers per Plant	Yield per Plant (Grams)	No. Tubers per Plant	Yield per Plant (Grams)
Heavy clay	3.1	195	3.0	377
Clay loam	4.2	387	4.9	664
Fine sandy loam	5.9	489	6.3	1034

It is fairly well known that loss from tuber rot caused by late blight, *Phytophthora infestans,* is usually more serious on heavy wet soil than on light or well-drained soil. Since infection is by the washing of the blight spores down through the soil onto the tubers, it might be supposed that the opposite would be true. In heavy soil, however, the soil particles are closer together, holding the moisture closer to the tuber and thus making conditions more favorable for tuber infection.

Soil Reaction

The relative acidity or alkalinity of the soil solution of any soil influences the development and sometimes the quality of the crop grown. Soil reaction is conveniently and accurately expressed as pH or hydrogen potential, a neutral soil being pH 7.0. Reaction values above 7.0 indicate alkalinity; those below express acidity. Very few soils used for potatoes are alkaline. To interpret pH values, one should know that pH 8.0 is strongly alkaline, 6.5 slightly acid, 5.5 moderately acid, 4.5 strongly acid. Among the commercially important vegetables, the potato is one of those most tolerant of soil acidity. It makes very satisfactory growth and yield at a pH range of 4.8 to 5.4.

When potatoes are grown in rotation with other crops which are much less tolerant of soil acidity, the problem of maintaining or adjusting to a satisfactory soil reaction is sometimes difficult. Practically, it is much more difficult and costly to acidify a soil that is not sufficiently acid than it is to reduce acidity of a soil that is too acid for any given crop. One reason for this is that lime in either hydrate or carbonate form is cheaper and safer to handle than sulfur in whatever form it may be used.

Aside from the fact that soil reaction influences yield of potatoes, it also influences the incidence of the scab disease. For the years 1931 and 1932, Blodgett and Howe (1934) surveyed the potato counties of New York to relate the lime requirement of the soil to the occurrence of scab on the potatoes sampled for those years. A total of 313 samples of 100 tubers each was examined. The results for the two years are summarized in table 15.

TABLE 15. RELATION OF pH OF SOIL TO SCAB ON 313 SAMPLES IN NEW YORK.

pH of Soil	1931		1932	
	Number of Samples	Scab in Per Cent	Number of Samples	Scab in Per Cent
4.33–5.44	53	3.3 ± 0.9	112	6.2 ± 1.0
5.45–7.49	61	18.7 ± 2.8	72	27.0 ± 2.6
7.50–8.35	9	8.8 ± 2.3	6	13.5 ± 4.3

The data in table 15 are consistent with those of many other workers in that they indicate that scab is usually more prevalent within a pH range of 5.5 to 7.4 than it is when the soil is either more or less acid.

Perhaps the most comprehensive studies of the relation of soil reaction to rate of growth, yield, and quality were those by Smith (1937, 1938). On a Dunkirk silt loam soil at Ithaca, he maintained 30 permanent soil reaction plots providing, by the use of sulfuric acid and hydrated lime, a pH range of 4.75 to 8.20. Five replications of each soil reaction were provided on a soil testing naturally about pH 5.4 to 5.7. At pH values lower than 4.9, fresh weight of tops and the tuber-top ratio were lower than at any higher value. Also, in the most acid plots the plants matured earlier than in plots of a medium reaction. "Plants growing in fairly alkaline soils, ranging from pH 7.79 to pH 8.36, produced fewer tubers, smaller tubers and lower total yields of tubers than did plants growing in less alkaline soils or acid soils above approximately pH 4.8 to 5.0." In general, the percentage of starch on the dry-weight basis in tubers grown at soil reactions ranging from pH 5.40 to 6.05 was higher than in tubers grown at either higher or lower pH ranges. Wessels (1932), similarly, working with permanent soil reaction plots on Sassafras silt loam soil on Long Island, maintained a pH range of 4.4 to 6.8. While the yield of scabby potatoes increased consistently from almost none at pH 4.4 to about 65 per cent of the crop at pH 6.8, every year the maximum total yield was obtained at pH 5.2 to 5.6. This relationship was also approximated by Smith (1938), whose results for 1932 to 1936 inclusive are shown in table 16.

To maintain the most favorable soil reaction for potatoes, growers should have their soil tested occasionally. This can be done fairly well by the colorimetric method but more accurately by some standard, electrically operated potentiometer. Recommendations for the adjustment of soil reaction should depend on the degree of correction to be made and the cost of the soil amendment to be used. At a pH below 4.8, lime may well be recommended, the amount depending on the type of soil and kind of lime used. At pH 4.9 to 5.3, a neutral fertilizer will aid in maintaining the present condition. Where the reaction is pH 5.4 to 5.8, an acidifying fertilizer such as ammonium sulfate, used in large quantity, should increase the soil acidity slightly. In situations where the pH ranges above

TABLE 16. RELATION OF SOIL pH TO YIELD AND SCAB AT
ITHACA, N.Y.

Year	pH Range	Total Yield		Per Cent Scabby	
		Highest	Lowest	Highest	Lowest
1932	4.7–7.5	5.0–7.5	4.7–4.9	6.1–6.5	4.7–4.9
1933	4.8–8.3	4.8–6.7	7.8–8.3	7.4–7.8	4.8–5.3 8.0–8.3
1934	4.8–8.4	4.8–6.9	8.2–8.4	6.9	4.8–5.0
1935	5.1–8.4	5.1–7.9	8.0–8.4	6.1–7.3	5.1–5.5 8.2–8.4
1936	4.7–7.9	4.7–5.0	7.8–7.9	6.2–6.7	4.7–5.0

5.8 and the grower is having difficulty with scab, he may use agricultural sulfur but only with caution and on the advice of good authority. Too much sulfur is not only toxic to plants but costly to use when applied in amounts of more than 500 pounds to the acre. A small amount mixed with the fertilizer and applied in bands along the row will acidify the soil solution in a localized area and will be sufficient to protect the newly developing tubers at their most scab-susceptible stage. Other phases of this subject are discussed in Chapter 4 under soil management.

REFERENCES

Blodgett, F. M., and F. B. Howe. Factors influencing the occurrence of potato scab in New York. Cornell Univ. Agr. Exp. Sta. Bul. 581, 1934.
Bushnell, John. Sensitivity of the potato plant to soil aeration. Amer. Soc. Agron. Jour. 27, No. 4, 1935.
Clark, Charles F. Development of tubers in the potato. U.S. Dept. Agr. Bul. 958, 1921.
Driver, C. M., and J. G. Hawkes. Photoperiodism in the potato. Imperial Bureau of Plant Breeding and Genetics (School of Agr., Cambridge, Eng.), 1943.
Edmundson, W. C. Time of irrigating potatoes as affecting stolon growth and tuber set and development. U.S. Dept. Agr. Circ. 496, 1938.
Fox, D. Scott. Analysis of the costs of growing potatoes. Unpublished thesis, Cornell University, 1918.

Garner, W. W., and H. A. Allard. Further studies in photoperiodism; the response of the plant to relative length of day and night. Jour. Agr. Research 23, 1923.

Hackborth, J. Versuche über photoperiodismus bei sudamerikanischen kartoffel-klonen. Zuchter 7, 1935.

Hardenburg, E. V. Some factors affecting tuber shape in potatoes. Potato Assn. of Amer. Proc., 1926.

McClelland, T. B. Studies of the photoperiodism of some cultivated plants. Jour. Agr. Research 37, 1928.

Metzger, C. H. Growing better potatoes in Colorado. Colo. Agr. Exp. Sta. Bul. 446, 1938.

Miller, J. C., and F. McGoldrick. Effect of day length upon the vegetative growth, maturity, and tuber characters of the Irish potato. Amer. Potato Jour. 18, 1941.

Schick, R. Über den Einfluss der Tageslange auf den Knollenansatz der Kartoffel. Zuchter 3, 1931.

Smith, J. Warren. Weather and yield of potatoes. U.S. Dept. Agr. Weather Bur. National Weather and Crop Bul. 19, Ser. 1916, July, 1916.

Smith, Ora. Effect of soil reaction on growth, yield and market quality of potatoes. Cornell Univ. Agr. Exp. Sta. Bul. 664, 1937.

Smith, Ora. Growth and development of the potato as influenced especially by soil reaction. Cornell Univ. Agr. Exp. Sta. Mem. 215, 1938.

Tincker, M. A. H. The effect of length of day upon the growth and reproduction of some economic plants. Ann. Bot. Lond. 39, 1925.

Werner, H. O. The effect of a controlled nitrogen supply with different temperatures and photoperiods upon the development of the potato plant. Nebr. Agr. Exp. Sta. Research Bul. 75, 1934.

Werner, H. O. Response of two clonal strains of Triumph potatoes to various controlled environments. Jour. Agr. Research 61, 1940.

Wessels, P. H. Soil-acidity studies with potatoes, cauliflower, and other vegetables on Long Island. Cornell Univ. Agr. Exp. Sta. Bul. 536, 1932.

CHAPTER 4

Rotation and Soil Management

POTATOES like other cultivated crops, if grown continuously
or often on the same land are likely to drain the soil of
mineral nutrients, to show an increase in the incidence of certain
diseases, and even to destroy good soil tilth unless preventive measures are used. In recent years, the trend has been toward more intensive potato production on the better-adapted soils and toward
larger acreage units on fewer farms. With this trend has come the
need to pay more attention to rotation of crops and to soil management.

ROTATION

By definition, rotation is a succession of different crops on the
same land over a period of years. For many years rotation was considered necessary for the maintenance of potato yields, and a
majority of growers included small grains followed by sod crops of
either legumes or grasses or both. Green-manure crops and winter-
cover crops were seldom grown and probably not much needed in
the system of farming then followed. More recently, results from
long-time rotation experiments, such as the one on Wooster silt
loam soil at the Ohio Experiment Station, have shown that soil
tilth or structure is probably the most important single factor related to benefits to be derived from rotation.

Advantages of Rotation

Among the advantages of rotation the following are listed as of
greater or less importance depending on soil type, rainfall, topog-
raphy, types of farming, and other factors pertinent to the locality:
(1) less drain on soil nutrients, (2) stabilization of farm income
through diversity of enterprises, (3) conservation of soil organic
matter by less frequent plowing and cultivation, (4) better control

of soil-borne diseases such as scab, rhizoctonia, Fusarium wilt, and nematodes, (5) better control of tuber injury from the wheat wireworm and the white grub, (6) better use of year-round farm labor, (7) soil conservation by better erosion control, (8) maintenance of better soil structure on the heavier soils.

Except on farms where environmental factors, soil type, and market facilities are ideally suited to intensive potato production, potato growing and dairy farming form a good combination.

Disadvantages of Rotation

Some of the more obvious disadvantages of a long rotation, which seem important to growers located under ideal conditions for potato growing, are the following: (1) more difficult control of such insects as the wheat wireworm and white grubs, (2) greater necessity for the use of fields where the soil is too heavy for potatoes, (3) production of low-income crops on land having a high real-estate value and high tax assessment, (4) competition with other farm enterprises for farm labor.

Production of tree fruits, especially of those which require timely spraying and harvesting labor, offers considerable competition for labor. For these and other reasons, potato production is less intensive in fruit growing areas and more intensive on Long Island, New York; in Aroostook County, Maine; in New Jersey, southern Idaho, and Kern County, California. Cabbage and potatoes often do not fit well into the same rotation because of the difficulty of controlling the clubroot disease of cabbage and the scab disease of potatoes. Where lime is applied to correct soil reaction for clubroot control, the situation is likely to be aggravated for the control of potato scab. According to Dykstra (1948), to avoid certain disease organisms potatoes should be rotated with nonsusceptible crops to eliminate or reduce potato-infecting organisms by starvation. Such diseases he lists as rhizoctonia canker, Fusarium wilt, and Verticillium wilt, and he indicates that a 3- to 5-year rotation is usually effective in their control.

Since the more acid soils are capable of producing maximum yields of smooth, bright-skinned tubers, there is some advantage in rotating with potatoes only those crops which have a similar soil adaptation so far as soil reaction is concerned. It is sometimes not practical to include crops having a high lime requirement in the potato rotation. This is especially true where the scab disease is troublesome. However, in the far West such crops as alfalfa and sweet clover often precede potatoes and are considered very desirable as a means of maintaining good yields and good soil tilth. Rotation of potatoes with crops which leave a large amount of organic matter in the soil is especially desirable on soils which are subject to puddling and on those which have a low porosity.

Types of Rotation

The popularity of any given rotation is usually contingent on the importance of other crops and on the type of agriculture common to the region. For irrigated potatoes in the Great Plains region of Nebraska, Colorado, Idaho, and Wyoming, the following 6-year rotation is recommended by Werner (1947): (1) potatoes, (2) sugar beets, beans, corn, tomatoes or other cultivated crop (manure ahead of this crop if available), (3) barley or peas (for canning), used as a nurse crop for alfalfa, (4) alfalfa, (5) alfalfa, (6) alfalfa. Such a cropping system provides good soil tilth, plenty of livestock feed, soil nitrogen, manure to maintain a high level of fertility, and assures a minimum of scab in the potato crop. Where potatoes are grown under dry-land conditions as in Nebraska, the best rotation is that which provides the greatest amount of subsoil moisture. In this case, preceding potatoes by a year of summer fallow has given higher average yields than preceding it by either corn or wheat.

In Aroostook County, Maine (Hawkins *et al.*, 1947) during the 10-year period 1935–1944, the trend has been toward more frequent cropping to potatoes on the same land. On eighty-two fields sampled, potatoes had been grown four to six times during the 10 years. This trend toward shorter rotations was undoubtedly encouraged by the relatively high price level during these later years. To compare potato yields from continuous cropping with those obtained under rotation, an experiment was set up by Chucka *et al.* (1943) at Presque Isle, Maine, in 1927, in which potato yields in a 3-year, a 2-year rotation, and a continuous cropping system were compared. Green Mountain variety was used, the results being measured over the 12-year period 1930–1941. For each potato crop, 2000 pounds to the acre of 4-8-7 fertilizer were applied. The 3-year rotation consisted of oats-clover-potatoes, while the 2-year cycle consisted of a green-manure crop followed by potatoes. For the 12-year period, the average yields for the 3-, 2-, and 1-year cropping cycles were 383, 404, and 351 bushels to the acre respectively. So long as the dairy industry is of minor importance in Aroostook County, Maine, and since tractors have largely replaced horses, there is little need to grow forage or small grain for feed. The superior yields of potatoes resulting from the 2-year rotation of potatoes and green manure, therefore, can be justified in this area. In this case, the green-manure crops most commonly plowed under are oats, crimson clover, mammoth clover, and buckwheat. The more favorable yields from the 2-year cycle were said to be due to the greater amount of organic matter supplied.

The effect of the crop preceding potatoes in the rotation on the yield of potatoes is difficult to measure. This is because many variables other than rotation per se can affect yield. However, a number of experiment stations have made studies of this kind. Mack, Stout, and Haller (1933) at State College, Pennsylvania, compared a number of vegetable crops in respect to their influence on the yield of crops following the next year in rotation. For the years 1930, 1931 and 1932, potatoes, tomatoes, and late cabbage significantly decreased the yields of other crops whereas early cabbage, carrots, onions, sweet corn, beans, and summer pumpkins usually did not show such effect. Similarly, Lea and Odland (1938) at the Rhode Island Station compared the yield of Green Mountain potatoes following several different vegetables. The yields of potatoes following mangel beets averaged considerably lower than when potatoes followed corn, rutabagas, or potatoes. The application of results such as these to general rotation practice is questionable. Rather it can be expected that the long-time effect of any given crop on the one immediately following will depend on the existing fertility level of the soil, the nutrient requirements of the rotated crops, and the quantity of nutrients currently supplied.

SOIL MANAGEMENT

Good management of a potato soil requires that it be so handled that it will produce its maximum yield of marketable tubers over the longest possible period of time. Such management involves the maintenance of good soil tilth or structure, soil reaction, and soil fertility. The last named, soil fertility, is least difficult to maintain because it can be done through the application of adequate commercial fertilizer of the right kind. To maintain or improve the structure of a too heavy soil is more difficult. Intensive cultivation of a fine silt loam soil tends to decrease its pore space and so cause it to puddle. The management of sandy loams and light soils in general is relatively easy. Such soils are naturally well aerated and have more pore space than do heavy soils. Because of the difficulty of changing the structure and the reaction of a soil, the original choice of soil for potato growing is especially important.

Among the methods possible to regulate soil tilth are tile drainage and the incorporation of organic matter in the form of either green-manure crops or farm manures. Soil reaction is regulated by the use of acidifying or alkalizing soil amendments such as sulfur, fertilizers and various forms of lime.

Organic Matter

Plant remains, when incorporated in the soil, are commonly referred to as organic matter. Upland or mineral soils contain from 1 per cent to 5 per cent of organic matter, and muck soils carry from 40 to 50 per cent of organic matter. Good yields of potatoes are obtained annually on the Sassafras silt loam and the Bridgehamton silt loam soils of Long Island, which analyze as low as 1.5 to 3.5 per cent of organic matter. Organic matter, however, is the principal source of soil humus from which the potato plant gets a part of its nitrogen. The principal function or value of organic matter in a potato soil, therefore, is to maintain a fairly stable nitrogen supply, to assist in the absorption and retention of soil moisture, to maintain and improve soil tilth, structure, pore space, or aeration, and to reduce soil erosion.

Bushnell (1935) demonstrated that lack of soil aeration was the principal cause of decreasing potato yields in the long-time rotation experiment on Wooster silt loam soil at the Ohio Agricultural Experiment Station. Using both plain and perforated drain tile in comparison with no tile (soil trenched and refilled) he varied the soil aeration and immediately increased the yield of potatoes in proportion to the soil aeration. The average total yield increases for 2 years were 11 per cent for the plain tile and 20 per cent for the perforated tile.

Green-Manure and Cover Crops

Important sources of organic matter on farms where the dairy industry is not large and where stable manure is not available are the green-manure and cover crops. The only difference between a green manure and a cover crop is that the latter occupies the soil over winter to prevent erosion and to aid in the retention of residual mineral fertilizer left from the previous crop. In the northern potato states, rye is the most satisfactory cover crop because it can be seeded

Fig. 15. Corn being plowed under as a soil-improving crop for potatoes.

late, germinates and grows well at low temperatures, and is not very subject to winter killing. In milder climates, other annual grasses and a few legumes are adapted to cover-crop usage.

According to Grantham, Millar, and Mick (1939), "The best way to increase the organic matter content of potato soils is to plow under sods of clover, alfalfa or sweet clover. More material is added if the entire crop is plowed under, as is done by some very successful growers. These legume crops, when inoculated, collect nitrogen from the air, and produce plant tissue rich in this element. As humus contains one pound of nitrogen to about 20 pounds of weight, the necessity of adding plant residues rich in nitrogen is apparent if the humus content of the soil is to be increased. Straw, corn stover, and similar nonleguminous plant materials contain only about one pound of nitrogen to 100 or 200 pounds of weight and, hence, are not very effective in building up the soil humus supply." This last statement should not be taken as an indictment of nonleguminous green manures for the potato grower. Many of the more acid soils used for potatoes are not well adapted for growing legumes. Liming would be impractical because of potato scab and the expense of continuous liming sufficient for legume growth. Under such conditions, it is more practical to grow nonlegumes such as corn stover, sunflowers, millet, or even mature rye. The best choice of green-manure crops may well be the one which will yield the greatest volume of dry matter in a single season. In this way, soil tilth can be maintained satisfactorily, provided adequate nitrogen is supplied in the commercial fertilizer, and provided sufficient nitrogen is broadcast over the green-manure crop before plowing to ensure

TABLE 17. GREEN-MANURE CROPS IN A 2-YEAR POTATO ROTATION, OHIO AGRICULTURAL EXPERIMENT STATION, 1933.

Green-Manure System	Yield and Composition of Green Manure Each Year			Potato Yield Following Year (Bushels)
	Dry Matter (Pounds)	Nitrogen (Pounds)	Nitrogen (Per Cent)	
Sweet Clover	6,000	150	2.5	202
Rye	2,000	60	3.0	
Soybeans	4,500	117	2.6	
Rye	4,000	80	2.0	
	10,500	257		233
Rye	2,000	60	3.0	
Buckwheat	3,000	66	2.2	
Buckwheat (second crop)	2,500	60	2.4	
Rye	4,000	80	2.0	
	11,500	266		249
Rye	2,000	60	3.0	
Sowed-corn	10,000	100	1.0	
Rye	4,000	80	2.0	
	16,000	240		258

rapid decomposition and the maintenance of a safe carbon-nitrogen ratio. By safe C/N ratio is meant that the proportion of carbon to nitrogen in the soil should not exceed 10 to 1, otherwise the micro-organisms which decompose the organic material will be unable to fulfill that function, and the potato crop will suffer from the lack of either nitrogen or water, or both. The comparative yield of dry matter and nitrogen and corresponding yields of potatoes obtained the following year by Bushnell (1933) from various green manures used on heavy silt loam soil at Wooster, Ohio, are shown in table 17.

Fig. 16. Rye is the most commonly grown winter cover crop in the North and East.

The data in table 17 indicate that on heavy soil where aeration is needed, potato yields are likely to be benefited in proportion to the amount of dry matter turned under. They also show that it is sometimes possible to produce as much or more nonleguminous organic matter as leguminous material. Some of these combinations, however, would require unnecessary expense for plowing. Instead of two crops of rye and a summer green-manure crop in a single year, the first crop of rye might well be left to mature a crop of grain. The rye grain cut high with a combine would furnish a cash crop, the straw going back onto the soil, enough grain self-seeded to furnish another cover crop, and only one plowing in a single year would be required. In this case, it might be advisable to broad-

TABLE 19. COMPARATIVE ANALYSIS OF 5–10–10 FERTILIZER AND COW MANURE.

Fertilizer Material	Analysis in Pounds			Ratio of N-P$_2$O$_5$-K$_2$O
	Nitrogen	Phosphoric Acid	Potash	
1 ton 5-10-10 fertilizer	100	200	200	1-2-2
10 tons mixed cow manure	118	30	90	4-1-3

especially in nitrogen. Poultry and sheep manures are comparatively high in ammonia and are therefore more likely to induce potato scab than ordinary dairy stable manure. Because of the alkalizing effect of the ammonia in fresh stable manure, such manure should not be applied just before potato planting because of the danger of scab. It is better to apply it several months before, or preferably on

Fig. 17. A badly eroded potato field planted up and down the slope.

the seeding one or two years before potatoes. Application of not more than 10 tons to the acre, evenly spread with a manure spreader, is desirable practice. Larger applications at one time have generally not shown a profitable yield increase as compared to smaller applications. Smith and McCubbin (1940) reported yields from a rotation experiment running through the years 1936–1939 inclusive, on well-aerated loam soils in Steuben and Franklin Counties, New

York. Highest average yields were obtained where potatoes were grown every year with 1000 pounds of 5-10-5 fertilizer and 12 tons of stable manure. In Steuben County the increase in yields from stable manure over yields from fertilizer alone was 72 bushels to the acre or 32 per cent; in Franklin County, 37 bushels to the acre or 13 per cent. The conclusion is that manure is usually superior to fertilizer in its benefits to the potato crop, but it must be so used as to avoid trouble with potato scab, and its cost of application is not always justified where the fertility level is already high, where the soil tilth is good, and where manure is not easy to procure.

Fig. 18. Potato rows planted on the contour to check downhill erosion.

Soil Conservation

A good potato soil, because of its friability, is especially subject to erosion. The erosion may be caused by wind, by surface runoff, or by gullying. The result is rapid loss of the best topsoil, mineral nutrients, moisture needed for plant growth, and organic matter. With the trend toward more intensive production on the best soils, the need to practice conservation methods becomes more acute. Good soil management therefore involves a program which will best ensure the long-time conservation of surface soil, soil nutrients, soil moisture, and soil organic matter consistent with good yields of high-quality potatoes. Maintenance of organic matter will not only help to hold the topsoil in place but make nitrogen and other nutrients available. Planting the potato rows on contour or at least crosswise of the slope of the land will aid in the control of surface erosion. The construction of terraces and diversion ditches is advised where potatoes are grown on hilly fields subject to washing. Strip cropping to provide a sod crop with alternate strips of potatoes is also a good way to check erosion. In short, soil conservation practices are essentially those necessary to the maintenance of high yields of potatoes.

Fig. 19. Strip cropping on steep land to check soil erosion; darker strips are in sod, lighter strips in potatoes. (Soil Conservation Department, Cornell Univ.)

REFERENCES

Bushnell, John. Unpublished data, Ohio Agr. Exp. Sta., 1933.

Bushnell, John. Non-legumes as green manures for potatoes. Amer. Soc. Hort. Sci. 33, 1935.

Bushnell, John. Sensitivity of the potato plant to soil aeration. Amer. Soc. Agron. Jour. 27, No. 4, 1935.

Chucka, Joseph A., Arthur Hawkins, and Bailey E. Brown. Potato fertilizer-rotation studies on Aroostook Farm, 1927–1941. Maine Agr. Exp. Sta. Bul. 414, 1943.

Dykstra, T. P. Production of disease-free seed potatoes. U.S. Dept. Agr. Circ. 764, 1948.

Goss, R. W. The effect of crop rotations on some soil-borne diseases of the potato. Ohio Vegetable Growers' Assn. Proc. 22, Ann. Meeting, 1937.

Grantham, G. M., C. E. Millar, and A. H. Mick. Soil management for potatoes. Mich. Agr. Exp. Sta. Special Bul. 299, 1939.

Hawkins, Arthur, Joseph A. Chucka, and A. J. MacKenzie. Fertility status of potato soils of Aroostook County, Maine, and relation to fertilizer and rotation practices. Maine Agr. Exp. Sta. Bul. 454, 1947.

Lea, G. F., and T. E. Odland. Effect of preceding crops on yields of Green Mountain potatoes. Amer. Potato Jour. 15, No. 6, 164–170, 1938.

Mack, Warren B., Gerald J. Stout, and Frank W. Haller. The effect of certain truck crops on the yield of truck crops following them on the same plots in the next season. Amer. Soc. Hort. Sci. Proc. 30, 447–451, 1933.

Metzger, C. H. Growing better potatoes in Colorado. Colo. Agr. Exp. Sta. Bul. 446, 1938.

Smith, Ora, and E. N. McCubbin. Potato rotation studies. Amer. Potato Jour. 17, No. 9, 235–243, 1940.

Werner, H. O. Commercial potato production in Nebraska. Nebr. Agr. Exp. Sta. Bul. 384, 1947.

Wessels, P. H. and John D. Hartman. Experiments with cover crops on Long Island. Cornell Univ. Agr. Exp. Sta. Bul. 677, 1937.

CHAPTER 5

Fertilization

THE USE of commercial fertilizer in potato growing is becoming increasingly important throughout the United States. More fertilizer is needed because the supplies of farm manures are dwindling, and because the natural fertility of our potato soils is decreasing as the intensity of production increases. Fairly large investment in fertilizer for the potato crop is justified, because the crop affords a relatively large gross return, because a large amount of nutrients is removed when the crop is harvested, and because the increase in yield usually justifies the expenditure.

The fertilizer requirements of a crop vary according to the size of plant produced, its gross yield of dry matter, its ability to forage for soil nutrients, and its capacity to synthesize and utilize plant food. When all conditions for growth are favorable, the yield of potatoes often approximates 400 to 500 bushels to the acre. Such a yield is possible only when all conditions are ideal throughout the growing season. The annual expenditure for fertilizer ranks the potato crop with cotton and corn.

Nutrient Requirements

Compared to most other important vegetable crops, the potato crop removes from the soil more total nutrients and a high ratio of potash. Based on the analysis of the harvested crop, the pounds of nitrogen, phosphoric acid, potash, calcium, and magnesium to the acre removed in an acre yield of potatoes are indicated in table 20.

Such data as those shown in table 20 are in no sense a good basis for buying or compounding a fertilizer mixture for a certain situation. They do indicate, however, the minimum quantity of each of these elements necessary in producing these yields. The extent to which these quantities of the respective nutrients should be supplied by commercial fertilizer depends on such other factors as the quantity already available in the soil and the environmental conditions that may limit yields.

TABLE 20. APPROXIMATE POUNDS PER ACRE OF NUTRIENTS
REMOVED BY CERTAIN CROPS.

Crop	Yield per Acre	N	P_2O_5	K_2O	CaO	MgO
Beans (dry)	17 bu.	68	19	34	8	5
Cabbage	15 tons	130	45	130	41	11
Corn (sweet)	5 tons	36	24	83	2	11
Onions	10 tons	57	15	47	14	6
Peas (green)	3000 lbs.	34	10	13	3	3
Potatoes	400 bu.	140	30	200	60	30
Tomatoes	10 tons	40	20	70	4	6

Nutrient Absorption

The selective absorption of nutrients by the potato plant is a controversial question, as is also true of other crop plants. The uptake of nutrients is not necessarily in accordance with what the plant needs for its maximum development and yield. Rather, it is influenced by the amount of available material in the soil, by soil moisture supply, by soil reaction, by soil aeration, by the amount of colloidal material in the soil, and to some extent by the nature and supply of cation or base exchange material present. In other words, it is possible to overfertilize potatoes or to apply so much nitrogen as to make the plant vegetative at the expense of tuber formation. It has been demonstrated that large yields of potatoes can be obtained in a very acid soil (pH 4.6–4.8), as on Long Island, when the supply of calcium is made adequate through large annual applications of complete fertilizer high in superphosphate.

According to Lorenz, working in Kern County, California (1944), the potato plant absorbs nitrogen most rapidly when it is developing fastest. This is usually during the period of 40 to 70 days after emergence. Adding nitrogen in the fertilizer increased nitrogen in all plant parts. Omission of phosphorus or potash did not affect absorption of nitrogen. The plant stems contained only 0.85 to 2.00 per cent of nitrogen late in the season as compared to 3 to 4 per cent early in the season. Omission of nitrogen from the fertilizer reduced the absorption of phosphorus by about the same amount as did the omission of phosphorus. At the last sampling, the leaves of the no-nitrogen plots contained 0.26 per cent of P_2O_5 compared to 0.29 per cent on the no-phosphorus plots and 0.40 per cent on the plots receiving both nitrogen and potash. The amount of potash in the fertilizer influenced the content of potassium in the leaves but was high in all plant parts. The potash content of the leaves increased from 4.0 per cent on April 5 to 4.5 per cent on May 28. It was about 8 per cent in the stems and petioles throughout growth. The magnesia content of the plant was not influenced by any variation in the amount of N, P_2O_5, and K_2O in the fertilizer. Although potash content increased from lowest in the leaves to highest in the tubers the reverse was true for magnesia. According to Lorenz, the magnesia content was 0.55 to 0.86 per cent in the leaves, 0.46 to 0.80 in the stems, 0.36 to 0.61 in the roots and 0.11 to 0.14 per cent in the tubers. Calcium was highest in plants receiving no nitrogen so far as leaves, stems, and roots were concerned, no difference appearing in the tubers.

Probably the most thorough study of the uptake and use of the principal nutrient elements by the potato plant under very favorable growth conditions was made by Hawkins (1946) in Aroostook County, Maine. His material consisted of the Green Mountain variety, fertilized with 2500 pounds of 4-8-8 fertilizer to the acre and yielding at the rate of 387 bushels. The planting date was May 18, the date of emergence June 16, or 29 days after planting. Hawkins found that the plant elaborated 50 per cent of its total dry matter during the period of 51 to 81 days after planting. Of the total amount of the six major elements absorbed during the season, 71 per cent was absorbed during this 30-day period. Obviously the absorption of nutrients is more rapid than the elaboration of dry matter during the early stages of growth, while the reverse is true during the latter part of the growth period. The total amount of the major elements found in the entire crop of 387 bushels, including all plant parts, was 143 pounds of nitrogen, 26 pounds of phosphoric acid, 232 pounds of potash, 56 pounds of calcium oxide, 30 pounds of magnesia, and 11 pounds of sulfur. The proportion of the absorbed nutrients that were translocated to the tubers was about as follows: ⅔ of the nitrogen, ⅘ of the phosphoric acid, ½ of the potash, $\frac{4}{10}$ of the magnesia, $\frac{1}{20}$ of the calcium oxide, and $\frac{6}{10}$ of the sulfur. The tubers of this 387-bushel crop contained 95 pounds of N, 20 pounds of P_2O_5, 117 pounds of K_2O, 3.2 pounds of CaO, 12 pounds of MgO, and 6 pounds of S. This indicates that N, P, and K are removed in the crop in the approximate ratio of 5-1-6. The absorption of nutrients by growth periods is shown in table 21.

TABLE 21. DRY MATTER PRODUCED PER ACRE AND NUTRIENTS ABSORBED BY GREEN MOUNTAIN POTATO PLANT (TUBERS AND ROOTS INCLUDED) DURING SUCCESSIVE INTERVALS OF GROWTH, 1939 (HAWKINS, MAINE).

Days after Planting	Dry Matter per Acre (Pounds)	Pounds Absorbed						
		N	P_2O_5	K_2O	CaO	MgO	S	Total
0–50	232	15.6	3.0	14.6	3.9	2.0	0.9	40.0
51–60	628	33.6	5.3	55.1	10.6	4.9	2.2	111.7
61–70	1191	37.6	5.7	64.1	15.7	8.8	2.7	134.6
71–81	1741	24.7	4.6	63.1	9.8	5.6	2.0	109.8
82–91	1419	14.0	4.3	17.5	10.1	4.5	0.7	51.1
92–101	1136	5.5	2.2	17.5	1.9	2.2	2.1	31.4
102–112	795	11.9	0.6	0.0	3.6	1.8	0.0	17.9
Totals	7142	142.9	25.7	231.9	55.6	29.8	10.6	496.5

Per Cent of Total

Days after Planting	Dry Matter per Acre	N	P_2O_5	K_2O	CaO	MgO	S	Total
0–50	3.2	10.9	11.7	6.3	7.0	6.7	8.5	8.1
51–60	8.8	23.5	20.6	23.8	19.1	16.4	20.8	22.5
61–70	16.7	26.3	22.2	27.6	28.2	29.5	25.4	27.1
71–81	24.4	17.3	17.9	27.2	17.6	18.8	18.9	22.1
82–91	19.9	9.8	16.7	7.6	18.2	15.1	6.6	10.3
92–101	15.9	3.9	8.6	7.5	3.4	7.4	19.8	6.3
102–112	11.1	8.3	2.3	0.0	6.5	6.1	0.0	3.6
Totals	100	100	100	100	100	100	100	100

Climatic and soil conditions greatly influence the absorption and utilization of fertilizer by the potato plant. This is well illustrated by MacGregor and Rost (1946), who reported on fertilizer tests conducted on three distinct soil types in the Red River Valley of northwestern Minnesota. There the soil is black and naturally high in organic matter and has a highly calcareous subsoil. Potato yields average low because of hot summers and a low rainfall, amounting to only about 16 inches for the 6-month growing season, April to September inclusive. The rotation is usually potatoes—small grain —sweet clover, the sweet clover being plowed in midsummer of the third year and the land left fallow the rest of the year. The soils are mainly of three types—loamy sand, silt loam, and silty clay loam. Although fertilizer has been used many years heavy applications do not pay, and most of the response is to potash rather than to either nitrogen or phosphorus. This is generally true of the potato-growing areas of northern Minnesota, North Dakota, and other parts of the famous Red River Valley. Results of fertilizer trials on twelve fields, with soil types including all three of the above, are reported by MacGregor and Rost. In these trials, using no nitrogen, 54 pounds of phosphoric acid, and 120 pounds of potash to the acre, each alone and in combination, only the potash gave any yield increase. The effect of soil type on yield and the absorption of P_2O_5 and K_2O into the plant are shown in table 22.

TABLE 22. EFFECT OF SOIL TYPE ON YIELD AND PERCENTAGE OF K_2O AND P_2O_5 IN OVEN-DRY TISSUE OF POTATO ROOTS AND LEAVES (AVERAGE OF BOTH FERTILIZED AND UNFERTILIZED PLANTS, RED RIVER VALLEY).

Soil Type	No. Plots Averaged	Yield per Acre (Bushels)	Increase, Per Cent	Per Cent in Oven-dry Matter			
				Roots		Leaves	
				K_2O	P_2O_5	K_2O	P_2O_5
Ulen loamy sand	9	149	—	1.25	0.323	2.27	0.461
Bearden silt loam	9	180	21	2.05	0.360	3.26	0.484
Fargo silty clay loam	18	265	78	2.40	0.317	3.47	0.486

The better yield on the heavier soil is explained on the basis that it contained more potash, potash being the limiting factor, and that more potash was absorbed into the roots and leaves. It is further explained that phosphoric acid was not responsible for any yield increase, because soil type showed no difference in its effect on the amount of this element absorbed by the plant.

Role of the Elements

All of the essential major and minor elements are, of course, necessary to maximum growth and yield of potatoes. Some, more than others, seem to evidence their specific function.

Nitrogen in abundance increases succulent, vegetative growth and may increase yield by lengthening the period of growth. It may delay maturity but, if by so doing, the yield is increased, the delay may be advantageous. An abundance of nitrogen, by stimulating vegetative growth, may also make conditions more favorable for the spread of late blight and virus diseases which are carried by aphids. A dense, succulent growth of foliage provides conditions less favorable for air drainage, for rapid drying of the plants, and for good coverage with fungicides and aphicides. Evidence to this effect was obtained by Hawkins, Terman, and Simpson (1947) of Maine. With Green Mountain variety fertilized with 1 ton to the acre of 3-8-10, 5-8-10, and 7-8-10 fertilizer, the incidence of mosaic in the crop grown the next year in Florida was 25, 28, and 45 per cent respectively.

Phosphoric acid, even though present in the potato plant in smaller quantity than either nitrogen or potassium, is often a limiting factor because insufficient amounts are available in the soil. Phosphoric acid functions in the formation of proteins, but there is little evidence that its deficiency limits the synthesis of carbohydrates. It is especially stimulating to root formation and promotes early maturity of the crop.

Potash is an important component of nearly all fertilizer mixtures and usually results in significant yield increases. It functions particularly in starch formation, yet nearly all fertilizer tests involving this element indicate that even as it increases yields, it adversely affects specific gravity and starch content of the tubers. This is well illustrated by Terman and Johnson (1947) who compared the specific gravity of the tubers from plots fertilized with potash varying from none to 300 pounds to the acre. Their results are shown in table 23.

It is generally known that potash fertilizer increases the blockiness or the ratio of thickness to length of tubers and roots. On the other hand, the influence of nitrogen and of phosphorus is to make

TABLE 23. RELATION OF POTASH IN THE FERTILIZER TO SPECIFIC GRAVITY OF TUBERS IN THE CROP (MAINE).

Pounds of K_2O in 1 Ton of Fertilizer	Specific Gravity of Tubers				Average
	Test 1	Test 2	Test 3	Test 4	
0 (5-8-0)	1.083	1.082	1.078	1.082	1.081
120 (5-8-6)	1.078	1.074	1.073	1.076	1.075
240 (5-8-12)	1.072	1.073	1.069	1.071	1.071
300 (5-8-15)	1.073	1.070	1.068	1.073	1.071

them more elongated. The effect of phosphoric acid and of potash in the fertilizer on the shape of potato tubers is shown by Prince *et al.* (1940) of New Hampshire in table 24.

TABLE 24. EFFECT OF PHOSPHORIC ACID AND OF POTASH ON THE SHAPE OF POTATO TUBERS (NEW HAMPSHIRE).

Fertilizer, 1 Ton per Acre	Number of Tubers Measured	Ratio of Length to Width of Tubers
4-8-7	479	1.30
4-16-7	239	1.34
4-8-14	249	1.23
4-16-14	268	1.27

The data in table 24 indicate that phosphoric acid tended to elongate the tubers while potash tended to make them shorter and blockier. Deficiency symptoms of the major elements—nitrogen, phosphoric acid, and potash—are better known than those of the minor elements. Still, many experienced growers are unfamiliar with them. Lack of nitrogen is evidenced by an abnormally light green or yellowish green color of the foliage and by a slow growth even in the presence of ample soil moisture. This is most likely to occur on the sandy soils after excessive rains which have leached the fertilizer. Phosphoric-acid deficiency is shown by an abnormally dark color of the leaves and subnormal growth, especially in heavy soils. The plant takes on an upright, staring appearance, and the tubers may have rust-brown lesions occurring internally. Lack of potash most likely to occur on the lighter, sandier soils is evidenced by stunted growth, a very dark green, bronzed leaf coloration and a downward turning of the leaflets.

Minor Elements

Potato yields have seldom been limited by deficiency of any of the minor elements. When this does occur, it is usually on the lighter soils and on soils which have been cropped intensively for many years and with insufficient fertilizer. According to Jones and Brown (1941), no case of boron, calcium, copper, or zinc deficiency has been found. In a few cases where the soil was overlimed, manganese deficiency symptoms developed because this element, under such conditions, was made relatively unavailable. Boron and zinc are most likely to become deficient under similar conditions, but the majority of potato acreage is grown on distinctly acid soil. Bear and Kitchen (1945) map the areas in the United States where symptoms of minor-element deficiency in potatoes have been reported. This map shows boron deficiency in northwestern Montana, manganese deficiency in the southern tip of South Carolina, and magnesium deficiency in all potato areas in Maine, Massachusetts, Connecticut, and the southern coastal plain soils of New Jersey, Virginia, North, and South Carolina. Aluminum and iron toxicity occurs only on the most acid soils and is easily corrected by ample applications of fertilizer containing lime or superphosphate.

Magnesium deficiency is evidenced in the leaves by a loss of green color first noticeable in the lower leaves, a dying of the tips and margins, and eventually a necrosis of the tissue between the veins. Lack of boron is usually first noticeable in the tubers, indicated by a tendency to slough the outer layer on cooking, by a brown discoloration beneath the skin, and by a tendency to sogginess and flat flavor. The development of fine feeding roots is retarded, and in severe cases there is a dieback of the growing points of the stem. Manganese deficiency in the potato plant is shown by a blanching or necrosis of the tissue between the leaf veins and is first noticeable in the upper plant parts.

Regional Fertilizer Practices

The analysis and the amount of fertilizer used on potatoes vary considerably in different regions of the United States. Differences in practice are justified on the basis of differences in rainfall, soil type, rotation, and types of farming.

In the northeastern, the middle Atlantic, and the southern states where rainfall is high, where the soils are leachy and erodible, and where cropping is intensive, relatively large applications are necessary. Farther west where rainfall is low and there is less leaching, less fertilizer is used. In Aroostook County, Maine, on Long Island, and in New Jersey and Virginia it is customary to apply at least a ton to the acre of such analyses as 5-10-5, 5-10-10, and 4-8-12. Many of the extensive growers in upstate New York and in Pennsylvania who have no stable manure also use these large applications. Dairy farmers in the East who rely on stable manure use 800 to 1200 pounds of 5-10-5 and 4-12-4. In Michigan on the sandier soils, 500 to 600 pounds of 3-12-12 are recommended. On the heavier soils less potash than this is needed, and, where manure is available, about 500 pounds of 4-16-8 is considered a good supplementary application. In the southern states where rainfall is high, applications of 600 to 2000 pounds to the acre of such analyses as 4-10-7, 4-12-4, 6-6-5, 6-8-4, and 6-8-6 are used. In the South where planters are not available, much fertilizer is applied ahead of planting by placing it in a furrow opened by a middlebuster or turn plow.

According to Werner (1947), in Nebraska where manure and alfalfa sod are turned under in the irrigated rotations, no increases in yield of potatoes are obtained from commercial fertilizer. Without manure or alfalfa, some profitable response is obtained from nitrogen and superphosphate. In western Nebraska, under dry land farming conditions, where no leaching has occurred, no fertilizer is used. Up to 1940 very little fertilizer was used on potatoes in Colorado, but the practice of using a little is gradually increasing. McLean, Sparks, and Binkley (1947) tested varying amounts of nitrogen, phosphoric acid, and potash on high pH soils in the famous San Luis Valley of Colorado. Here the soils vary from gravelly to adobe. Best results were obtained from 200- to 500-pound applications of 10-18-5. On the irrigated soils of southern California including the famous Kern County region, no potash is used, but enough sulfate of ammonia and superphosphate to supply about 100 pounds each of nitrogen and phosphoric acid per acre is applied. The usual practice is to apply 400 to 800 pounds of 16-20-0.

On the black soils of the Delta region near Stockton, California, no nitrogen is used, the application generally being 500 to 1000 pounds of 0-21-21, 0-10-12, or 0-16-20 to the acre.

Choice of Fertilizer

Until recently, growers were influenced in their choice by the brand on the bag. For the dealer, it was easier to sell the potato grower if the brand indicated a special mixture for that crop. Today, fertilizer is purchased, advisedly, not so much on the basis of the crop to be fertilized as on the basis of conditions under which it is to be grown. Good advice to the potato grower as to analysis, source of ingredients, and rate of application is hardly possible without knowledge of soil type, use of manure, cropping system, and previous fertilizer treatment of the field to be planted.

Light soils are likely to be more deficient in nitrogen and potash than are heavy soils. Phosphoric acid is often a limiting factor in heavy soil, because it is easily rendered unavailable, especially if the soil is quite acid. So it is that on Long Island and in other Atlantic seaboard soils, fertilizers relatively high in nitrogen and potash are used. On the heavier soils farther inland, the ratio of phosphoric acid is higher. On very acid soils, ingredients which tend to lessen acidity, such as nitrate of soda or even ground limestone, may be advised as materials in the formula. On the other hand, if increased soil acidity would help solve the scab control problem, sulfate of ammonia or ammonium nitrate should be used as sources of nitrogen. Where the rotation includes legumes or other sod crops, less nitrogen in the fertilizer and also less fertilizer will be needed. If potatoes or other cultivated row crops are grown often in the rotation, it is likely that more fertilizer and particularly more nitrogen will be needed than otherwise. Frequent and heavy applications of fertilizer to a soil may result in a surplus accumulation of available potash above the needs of the potato crop. Thus it is that the ratio of potash may well be reduced for a year or two until the surplus is exhausted. Such instances are numerous on Long Island and on muck soils where it is customary to apply a ton or more of complete fertilizer every year.

Basic to a wise choice of fertilizer for the potato crop is a knowledge of what is meant by such terms as ratio, analysis, formula, and concentration. *Ratio* refers to the proportion of nitrogen to phosphoric acid and to potash in the mixture. Such ratios as 1-2-1, 1-2-2, and 1-2-3 are illustrated by the analyses 5-10-5, 5-10-10, and 4-8-12 respectively. These are all commonly used by potato growers in the East. *Formula* refers to the ingredients or carriers of nitrogen, phosphoric acid, and potash used in making the mixture. To compound a ton of 5-10-10 fertilizer, one might resort to the formula: 500 pounds ammonium sulfate (20 per cent N), 1000 pounds superphosphate (20 per cent P_2O_5), 333 pounds muriate or chloride of potash (60 per cent K_2O), and 167 pounds of ground limestone or other filler. By *concentration* is meant the number of units of plant-food elements in the analysis. For example, a 10-20-10 fertilizer is of the same ratio (1-2-1) as a 5-10-5 analysis, but it contains twice as many units of plant food and is known as a double-strength fertilizer. Concentrated fertilizer is cheaper per unit of nu-trients contained, because it costs no more to manufacture and it affords a saving on transportation and labor to apply. Concentrated fertilizers have usually given about the same results as ordinary mixtures, although they are of necessity compounded of differ-ent ingredients and carry fewer impurities and minor elements. This is illustrated by a comparison made on Sassafras loam soil on Long Island, the results of which are shown in table 25.

TABLE 25. RELATION OF CONCENTRATION OF FERTILIZER TO YIELD OF POTATOES—A COMPARISON OF SINGLE-, DOUBLE-, AND TRIPLE-STRENGTH MIXTURES. (LONG ISLAND VEGETABLE RESEARCH FARM, RIVERHEAD, N.Y.).

Analysis	Acre Application (Pounds)	Yield per acre in bushels			
		1931	1932	1933	3-Year Average
5-8-7	2400	316	326	287	310
10-16-14	1200	323	315	295 *	311
15-24-21	800	320	311	225	285

* Application was 1400, instead of 1200, pounds to the acre.

In compounding a fertilizer, one may choose between organic and inorganic sources of nitrogen, depending on one or the other or a portion of both. Organic sources such as fish scrap, dried blood, and tankage are more expensive than inorganic sources but may have the advantages of better conditioning the mixture and making the nitrogen more slowly available. Brown (1926) reported the results of comparative tests at ten locations over a period of years on six important potato soil types. On the average, there was no significant difference in yields. Similarly one may choose between different sources of potash. Many comparative tests of muriate of potash, sulfate of potash, and sulfate of potash-magnesia have been made. Except where magnesium is a limiting factor, there have been no significant differences in yield. Muriate of potash (KCl) is the cheapest source and is the one most commonly used. There is some evidence that sulfate of potash (K_2SO_4) gives a somewhat higher starch content and a smoother-skinned tuber than does the muriate form.

Rate of Application

The amount of fertilizer one is justified in applying to an acre of soil for potatoes depends on the concentration of the mixture, on the need for available nutrients not naturally present, on the amount of rainfall common to the locality to make the fertilizer available, on the returns to be expected from the investment in the fertilizer, and whether other conditions are likely to limit the yield. As already stated, much larger amounts are applied in the East and South than in the Great Plains area and in the Pacific Coast states. The average amount is increasing as the intensity of cropping increases and as the average farm value of the crop remains relatively high.

In Michigan, Grantham, Millar, and Mick (1939) concluded that, because of limited rainfall, applications larger than 500 to 600 pounds to the acre of 3-12-6, 4-16-8, 3-12-12, and similar analyses were not justified on the soils where extensive tests were made. Specialized growers in Maine and along the Atlantic Coast often use more fertilizer than necessary but do so with the idea that such practice is good insurance for maximum yields at a time when the value of the crop is high. A good example of diminishing returns from increasing applications of fertilizer is shown by 12 years of testing at Presque Isle, Maine, by Chucka, Hawkins, and Brown (1943). Average yields from the use of 4-8-7 fertilizer in amounts ranging from none to 3000 pounds to the acre are shown in table 26.

TABLE 26. EFFECT OF VARYING AMOUNTS OF 4–8–7 FERTILIZER ON YIELD OF POTATOES AT AROOSTOOK FARM, PRESQUE ISLE, MAINE.

4-8-7 Fertilizer Pounds per Acre	Average 1930–1941 Inclusive		
	Bushels	Barrels	Per Cent of Check *
None	123	45	32
1500	346	126	91
2000	381	139	100
2500	397	144	104
3000	419	152	110

* Standard application of 2000 pounds used as check.

Analyzing the data above, the increase from each 500-pound increment is apparent up to 3000 pounds, but the increases beyond the 2000-pound application may not be economically profitable when potatoes are cheap.

In contrast to growers who use these large amounts, the majority of small growers use very little. Many of them are dairymen and depend on stable manure. Since manure is deficient in phosphoric acid, and since most dairy farms are composed of heavy soils, it is feasible to suggest that either the manure be reinforced with 50 pounds of superphosphate to the ton, or that these growers apply at least 500 pounds of a highly phosphatic fertilizer in the row at planting time. Such fertilizer might well analyze 4-12-4 or 4-16-4. Growers on naturally infertile soil, and who have no stable manure, sometimes rely on only 500 to 800 pounds of fertilizer to the acre. Few, if any, results should be expected. If the soil is heavy, phosphoric acid is limited and the little carried by the fertilizer may become "fixed" or unavailable to the potato crop. It is sometimes difficult to convince the grower who is getting no results that a larger application would be beneficial.

Method of Application and Placement

Years ago, it was customary to place a small amount of fertilizer or perhaps dried fish in the "hill" or directly beneath the seed piece. With the advent of large acre applications, the question of how to place the fertilizer has become important. The efficiency of the method of fertilizer application is most influenced by soil type, rainfall, and the amount of fertilizer applied. Fertilizer should be so applied as to encourage a maximum spread and development of root system and to avoid injury by contact with a too high concentration. The "split application" method, or placing a portion along the row and broadcasting the remainder, is slowly being adopted in the East where more than a half-ton to the acre is used. Applying a part of it deeply, encourages the development of a

Fig. 20. A fertilizer-spreading truck is an efficient means of broadcasting fertilizer on land to be later plowed for potatoes.

deeper root system, thus enabling the plant to withstand drought better. Beneficial effects of deep application are usually most noticeable in a dry season. In a wet season, the root system is generally shallow, and deep application may then show no results. Broadcasting a portion and applying a portion rather deeply is probably more appropriate in a heavy than in a light soil because in the heavy soil, movement of the dissolved fertilizer is less rapid. For best results with row application, the fertilizer should be placed 2 to 3 inches on either side of and a little deeper than the seed piece. To accomplish deep application, the planter should be equipped with large-sized opening discs. Sometimes it seems desirable to apply part of the application on the plow sole or bottom of the plow furrow. Fertilizer attachments for the plow are now available for this purpose. Most commercial growers apply only in equal depth bands from the fertilizer attachment on the planter. Unequal depth band placement, or the hi-lo band method, is accomplished by use of un-equal-sized opening discs. Smith, Hommel, and Kelly (1943) using both 800- and 1600-pound applications of 5-10-10 fertilizer on both Sebago and Rural varieties compared yields from three methods of placement: (1) equal depth bands, (2) hi-lo bands, and (3) one-half in equal depth bands and one-half broadcast before plowing. When the fertilizer was applied all in equal depth bands, the yields were as high with 800 pounds as with 1600 pounds. However, the results were somewhat in favor of the 1600-pound application when it was applied in hi-lo bands and much more so when it was applied half in bands and half by broadcast. In a later experiment at the Cornell Agricultural Experiment Station, Smith compared 1200 pounds and 2400 pounds of 5-10-10 fertilizer applied (1) all in bands, (2) one-half in bands and one-half broadcast, and (3) one-half in bands and one-half on the plow sole. With both rates of application, the split applications gave yields superior to those from placement all in bands. Differences between part broadcast and part on the plow sole were in both cases in favor of the former but not significantly so. Using specialized equipment for a study of nu-merous methods of placement Cumings and Houghland (1939) came to the following conclusions:

(1) Placement over, under, or mixed with the soil around the seed piece delayed emergence and decreased yield.

(2) Bands on each side of the seed piece gave best yields and earliest emergence.

(3) Bands on one side only gave lower yields than bands on both sides.

(4) Double-strength fertilizer in amounts equivalent to single strength gave equivalent results.

(5) Intermittent bands opposite each seed piece resulted in no advantage over continuous bands.

Muck and Peat Soils

There are millions of acres of still undeveloped peat soil in the United States, much of it in the region of the Great Lakes. When first broken for cultivation, peat soil is not well oxidized, and about three years are required before yields approach maximum. The potato crop grown on muck soils is limited by early killing frosts in some areas, but generally the crop is planted earlier than that on upland soil in the same region. Thus it is that muck-grown potatoes are often harvested immature and put on the early market. Because they contain considerably more organic matter than upland or mineral soils, virgin muck and peat soils are generally rather high in nitrogen and low in phosphoric acid and potash. Thus it is that fertilizers used on these soils are generally low in nitrogen and high in the other two elements. As these soils become older from the standpoint of cropping history, the need for nitrogen increases, and the residual supply of phosphoric acid and potash is built up through continued use of fertilizer. The reaction range of most muck soils is pH 4.0 to 7.5, most of those under cultivation being distinctly acid. Even the more acid mucks underlain with marl, will remain acid if the subsoil is not disturbed.

In Michigan the recommended fertilizer practice for growers of muck potatoes is 400 to 800 pounds of 0-8-32 fertilizer on deep high-lime mucks and the same amount of 0-8-24 on the more acid or low-lime mucks. Similar practices are followed on the peat soils of southern Minnesota. In New York where most of the muck soils have been in production longer, it is customary to apply about 2000 pounds of 4-8-12 fertilizer to the acre, applying all of it with the planter at planting time. Field experiments by the Cornell Agricultural Experiment Station showed that this practice is justified on the older mucks except for a tendency to accumulate some surplus of potash. A year or two of using 4-8-8 or 5-10-10 is suggested as a means of using up this surplus. More nitrogen and less potash is generally needed for potatoes grown on the older muck soils.

REFERENCES

Bear, Firman E., and Herminie Broedel Kitchen. Minor elements, evidence and concepts on functions, deficiencies and excesses. Baltimore, Md.: The Williams and Wilkins Company, 1945.

Brown, B. E. Comparative effectiveness of organic and inorganic fertilizer mixtures in potato production. Potato Assn. Amer. Proc., 13th Ann. Meeting, 1926.

Chucka, Joseph A., Arthur Hawkins, and Bailey E. Brown. Potato fertilizer-rotation studies on Aroostook Farm, 1927–1941. Maine Agr. Exp. Sta. Bul. 414, 1943.

Cumings, G. A., and G. V. C. Houghland. Fertilizer placement for potatoes. U.S. Dept. Agr. Tech. Bul. 669, 1939.

Grantham, G. M., C. E. Millar, and A. H. Mick. Soil management for potatoes. Mich. Agr. Exp. Sta. Special Bul. 299, June, 1939.

Hawkins, Arthur. Rate of absorption and translocation of mineral nutrients by potatoes in Aroostook County, Maine, and their relation to fertilizer practices. Jour. Amer. Soc. Agron. 38, No. 8, August, 1946.

Hawkins, Arthur, G. L. Terman, and G. W. Simpson. Effect of rate of fertilizer application on spread of leafroll and mosaic. Maine Agr. Exp. Sta. Bul. 449, June, 1947.

Hawkins, Arthur, Joseph A. Chucka, and A. J. MacKenzie. Fertility status of potato soils of Aroostook County, Maine, and relation to fertilizer and rotation practices. Maine Agr. Exp. Sta. Bul. 454, 1947.

Jones, H. A., and B. E. Brown. Hunger signs in crops—plant-nutrient deficiency symptoms in the potato. Washington, D.C.: Judd and Detweiler, pp. 99–124, 1941.

Lorenz, O. A. Potato nutrition studies. Amer. Potato Jour. 21, No. 7, July, 1944.

MacGregor, J. M., and C. O. Rost. Effect of soil characteristics and fertilization of potatoes as regards yield and tissue composition. Jour. Amer. Soc. Agron. 38, No. 7, July, 1946.

McLean, John G., Walter C. Sparks, and A. M. Binkley. Fertilizer studies with the Red McClure and Bliss Triumph varieties of potatoes in the San Luis Valley. Colo. Agr. Exp. Sta. Tech. Bul. 35, 1947.

Prince, Ford S., Paul T. Blood, W. H. Coates, and Thomas G. Phillips. Experiments with potatoes. N. H. Agr. Exp. Sta. Bul. 324, 1940.

Smith, Ora, R. F. Hommel, and W. C. Kelly. Relation of rate and placement of fertilizer, variety, seed spacing, and size of seed piece to yields of potatoes. Amer. Potato Jour. 20, No. 10, 1943.

Terman, G. L., and P. L. Johnson. Effect of rate of fertilizer application on specific gravity of potato tubers. Maine Agr. Exp. Sta. Bul. 449, pp. 312–313, 1947.

Werner, H. O. Commercial potato production in Nebraska. Nebr. Agr. Exp. Sta. Bul. 384, 1947.

CHAPTER 6

Seed

THE POTATO is one of the few important vegetables not ordinarily produced from true seed. Botanically, it is an annual because it blossoms, fruits, and dies in a single year. Practically, it is a perennial because the same parent stock is carried over from year to year by vegetative cuttings or seed pieces. Either the whole tubers or vegetative cuttings from them are what are commonly referred to as "seed" potatoes. Because of their vegetative character, seed-potato tubers are perishable and are subject to the invasion of diseases and insect pests and the influences of adverse storage conditions.

Definition

Good seed can be defined as that which is inherently high yielding, free from disease, true to varietal type, and in good physical condition. This being true, quality in seed potatoes is dependent as much on heritable factors and internal characters as on physical condition and external characters. Growers of certified seed constantly strive to ensure all four of the characteristics mentioned above.

Causes of Degeneration

Constant attention to disease and insect control and to conditions of growth and storage seem to be essential to the maintenance of good seed. There is no denying that virus diseases such as leaf roll, mosaic, spindle tuber, and yellow dwarf are important causes of degeneration of potato seed stocks. In even the most favorable potato-growing regions, these diseases are present and, as rapidly as insect vectors and weather conditions favor their spread, cause a decline in the value of the seed. The influence of environment or "place-effect" on degeneration, however, has been a controversial question. Northern-grown seed is very generally used by southern growers, and even though it costs a premium price the results usually justify its use. Such seed usually carries less virus disease because climatic conditions in the North are less conducive to the spread of the disease. It is conceivable also that a portion of the superiority of this northern-grown seed is due to its better sprout condition at the time it is planted in the South. Werner (1926) provided a good summary of the evidence on various factors affecting quality of seed potatoes. Prior to 1913, many research workers re-

Fig. 21. Healthy, high-yielding seed is necessary to profitable production. *Left:* two rows from home-grown seed. *Right:* two rows from certified seed.

ported superior results from northern seed and attributed the superiority to "place-effect" without regard to content of virus disease. It was even shown that seed which had degenerated in yield under ordinary cultivation in Nebraska was regenerated by a single year of mulching under straw. Such regeneration could hardly be possible if virus diseases were present. Werner compared seed stocks of both Early Ohio and Irish Cobbler varieties grown the previous year at different latitudes, from different dates of planting and harvesting, under dry-land and irrigated conditions, and of different degrees of maturity. He found that differences in yield were all apparently related to the amount of spindle tuber disease in the seed and concluded that disease rather than environment was responsible for differences in quality of the seed planted.

Condition Factors

The performance of any lot of seed potatoes is influenced by its readiness to sprout or by its sprout condition. Ideal seed is that which at the time of planting has at least one good sprout ready to grow rapidly from each eye of the seed piece. Whether seed is in good sprouting condition depends on such factors as rest period, after-ripening, dormancy, apical dominance, and multiple sprouting.

The tubers of the potato plant will not sprout immediately after its maturity because they are in a rest period. Although the length of this rest period varies with different varieties and with conditions of storage under normal conditions it is of about six weeks' duration. It is because of this rest period that southern growers find it difficult to use tubers recently harvested from their main crop for seed to plant the second crop. Rest period should be distinguished from dormancy. Dormancy is the entire period in the storage life of the potato tuber during which it is not developing sprouts.

It sometimes happens that potato tubers matured in hot, dry soil will sprout before they are harvested. This undesirable condition results from the fact that the rest period was broken early by high-temperature acceleration of the respiration rate. Appleman (1914) was one of the first to study the internal changes or the after-ripening processes which occur during the rest period. His object was to determine what changes are responsible for release of the growth processes. He arrived at three principal conclusions, (1) enzyme activity is not important, as breakage of the rest period is not accompanied by the production of diastase, (2) light induces photosynthetic activity, resulting in oxygenation of the tissue, (3) the length of the rest period is conditioned upon oxygen absorption. Rest period may be broken by any means which promotes the absorption of oxygen, such as high storage temperature, prevention of suberization of the outer tissues, use of anaesthesia, and cutting, peeling, or wounding of the tuber.

A number of investigators have worked with oxidizing agents to determine efficient methods of shortening the rest period. Among these are Denny (1926) and Stuart and Milstead (1934). After testing 224 substances, Denny found that ethylene chlorhydrin and the thiocyanates of sodium and potassium were most effective in breaking the rest period. Later he decided that thiourea was very useful as a means of increasing the number of sprouts and likewise the set of tubers. Stuart and Milstead found that some varieties had a much shorter rest period than others and agreed with Denny on the efficacy of the above chemicals.

Apical dominance refers to the tendency of the buds at the apical end of the tuber to develop ahead of and to dominate the growth of buds in the basal or stem end portion of the tuber. Appleman (1924) was one of the first to show that apical dominance can be used as an indication of vigor in the uncut seed tuber. Stored seed tends to lose its apical dominance with age. This tendency is evident when many of the eyes develop sprout growth late in the storage period, and the sprouts at each eye become smaller and more numerous. A disease known as hairsprout or spindling sprout is the extreme opposite of apical dominance and makes the tuber unfit for seed.

Three theories have been advanced to explain apical dominance, namely, (1) that the buds at the apex of the tuber have a morphological advantage, (2) that the apical buds produce an inhibiting substance or hormone which travels toward the basal buds, and (3) that a greater osmotic pressure in the apical tissue causes a flow of nutrients toward the apical buds.

Some of the workers who have worked with oxidizing agents to break the rest period and increase sprout numbers have concluded that apical dominance is destroyed as the auxin or growth inhibitor produced by the apical buds is destroyed. Other and more common methods of destroying apical dominance are (1) by continuous removal of successive generations of sprouts, (2) by long storage in a cool moist place, (3) by storage at high temperatures, and (4) by transverse cutting of the tuber. Whereas a whole seed tuber in apically dominant condition might produce a single-stemmed plant, cutting it into one-eye pieces would probably result in a plant from every piece.

The number of tubers borne by a potato plant, the average size of the tubers, and the percentage of No. 1 size tubers in the crop are greatly influenced by the number of sprouts from each seed piece and the number of stems to each plant. This factor of sprout number or multiple sprouting has been studied by Bushnell (1929) and others in relation to length of storage period or date of planting, storage conditions, maturity of the seed at time of harvest, greensprouting, size of seed piece, and treatment with thiourea. In brief, the effect on number of sprouts per seed piece or number of stems per plant is as follows: sprout number increases with length of storage period or lateness of planting and also with increase in storage temperature. When difference in maturity of the seed is due to difference in date of planting the previous season, the more mature seed produces the greater sprout number. Greensprouted seed resulted in no consistent difference in sprout number from that of ungreened seed, while sprout number increased with increase in size of seed piece. Using the recommended 1-per-cent thiourea soak treatment to increase sprout number, Bushnell soaked 50-gram cut pieces from 1 to 36 hours. In comparison with the untreated seed having an average sprout number of 1, soaking the seed, 1, 2, 12, and 36 hours increased the number to an average of 2.0, 2.3, 5.0, and 6.0 sprouts respectively per seed piece.

Quality Factors

Quality in seed potatoes is measured largely in terms of two factors, namely, freedom from disease and physical condition or freedom from mechanical injury and excessive sprouting.

Since virus diseases such as leaf roll and mosaic are impossible to detect in the tuber, and since both of these significantly reduce yield, it is especially important that their presence in seed potatoes be noted. The yield of a plant infected with leaf roll is reduced about 50 per cent, that of one with mosaic about 30 per cent. Pathologists are fairly well agreed that whenever the content of leaf roll in a strain or stock of seed exceeds 10 per cent, the seed should be discarded, and purchase of cleaner or certified seed at the usual premium price will be justified. Other seed-borne diseases including bacterial ring rot, yellow dwarf, spindle tuber, and blackleg may also be serious, and the tolerance on any one of them in certified seed is accordingly either zero or very small.

The effect of desprouting or the removal of successive generations of sprouts from stored seed potatoes may in time reduce vitality and cause the formation of weak sprouts or even sprout tubers. However, it has been shown that the removal of two or three generations does not usually cause any significant loss in vigor. Lombard (1938) removed three sets of sprouts each averaging about 2 inches in length from both Irish Cobbler and Green Mountain varieties and found no significant difference in either yield or storage shrinkage over a period of three years. Similarly, Westover (1928), using Rural potatoes, found no loss in yield from the removal of one generation of sprouts but concluded that seed tubers desprouted more than once have very little value as seed stock. Unless the sprouts on seed potatoes are so long as to interfere with their being fed through a machine planter, there is probably no point in removing them.

The soundness or physical condition of seed potatoes is more important in relation to perishability after planting than in relation to appearance. Bruised and broken tubers are more likely to rot both in storage and after planting because rot organisms of several diseases can more easily gain entrance. Fusarium rots have been especially prevalent and disastrous, and these are commonly associated with bruises. Late blight rot in seed should be avoided not alone because it may destroy the cut seed piece later, but also because it furnishes a source of infection of the growing crop. Badly shriveled or badly sprouted seed tubers can cause a poor stand of weak plants, if they are planted in dry hot soil where lack of moisture interferes with early growth. Otherwise, slightly spongy or shriveled seed does not mean loss in seed value.

Sources and Kinds

Users and particularly buyers of seed potatoes have a choice of many sources and kinds. In the northern states and in Canada it is usual for growers to use a portion of their own crop for seed. South of latitude 42° most stocks of seed are renewed every year. Out of the demand for superior northern-grown seed a very extensive trade in certified seed has developed since 1914. The buyer may choose to consider whether he will have immature or mature, mulched or open-cultivated, muck or upland-grown, irrigated or dry-land, certified or uncertified, northern- or southern-grown, or second-crop stock. The comparative qualities of each of these are of interest to the student of seed potatoes.

Immature seed is seed taken from plants that are not mature or dead at time of harvest. The seed may be immature because of late planting or early harvesting. In either case, it must and will mature in storage in the sense that its rest period will be accomplished, and sprouts will develop. Results of many tests comparing mature with

immature seed have been reported. Typical of these are the yields
reported by Martin of New Jersey (1921) in table 27.

TABLE 27. RELATION OF MATURITY OF SEED TO CROP GROWN
FROM IT.

Stage of Harvest of Seed Crop Grown in 1920	Yield of seed, 1920 (Bushels per Acre)	1921 Crop (Bushels per Acre)
2 weeks after blossoming	125	271
4 weeks after blossoming	157	260
24 per cent of leaves dead	207	250
50 per cent of leaves dead	258	243
92 per cent of leaves dead	281	216
100 per cent of leaves dead	281	196

The superiority of immature seed as shown above seems convinc-
ing, in spite of the fact that the cost was increased by the sacrifice
in yield resulting from early harvesting. Differences in yield, according to Martin, were not due to any difference in virus disease
content because no disease was present in any of the seed. All lots
of seed were stored in well-ventilated common storage until fall,
after which they were held in cold storage until planted. That
differences were due to differences in composition of the seed tubers
is also doubtful. Appleman and Miller (1926) analyzed potato
tubers at successive digging dates and at both the beginning and
the end of the rest period. They concluded that "by the end of the
rest period immature potatoes large enough for seed have practically
the same percentage composition and respiratory response as potatoes allowed to mature on the vine if both are stored under the same
conditions." It therefore appears that when difference is not due
to virus disease, the superiority of immature seed, if any, must be
explained on the basis of better sprout development or better
physical condition of the seed at planting time.

Southern growers usually plant northern-grown seed. They have
found by experience that it contains less virus disease, and that the
yields from it are enough larger to more than justify the cost. In
the East, growers on Long Island and in areas south of it depend
largely on seed grown in Maine, the maritime provinces of Canada,
New England, or upstate New York. In the central west, much of

the seed planted south of Nebraska and the Ohio River is grown in Michigan, Wisconsin, Minnesota, North Dakota, and the Red River Valley of Canada. Similarly, in the far West, seed planted in Kern County, California, has been grown mostly in northern California, or in the Klamath area of Oregon and Washington. Aside from the disadvantage of more virus disease in home-grown seed, the southern grower also would have the problem of holding his seed over a comparatively long period of hot weather or the expense of storing it in cold storage. As an alternative to buying northern-grown seed, the southern grower occasionally uses second-crop seed. Second-crop seed is produced by planting a second crop soon after the first or main crop is harvested. Being planted late this second crop does not mature before harvest, its tubers are usually small, and its yield is low. This makes it relatively expensive, but the grower is saved the expense of buying certified seed from the North. Second-crop seed sometimes yields as well as northern seed, but, being immature, it is usually slow to emerge, and the resulting delay may prove to be a distinct disadvantage. H. S. Cunningham of the Long Island Vegetable Research Farm at Riverhead, New York, reported results of a test made in 1943 of northern grown Cobbler seed compared with second-crop seed of the same strain. His results are summarized in table 28.

TABLE 28. COMPARISON OF YIELDS FROM NORTHERN-GROWN AND SECOND-CROP COBBLER SEED ON LONG ISLAND.

Kind of Seed	Yield in Bushels per Acre		
	Harvested July 1	Harvested July 14	Harvested August 9
Northern-grown	101	263	259
Second-crop	67	228	242

In the comparison above, there was much more virus disease in the Long Island grown second-crop seed; plants from it emerged later and stayed green a week longer. That it produced a later maturing crop is indicated by the fact that there was no increase in yield from the northern-grown seed after July 14, while that from the second-crop seed increased about 6 per cent.

Certified seed is seed that has been inspected, both while growing and after harvest, by qualified inspectors employed by an official certification agency, and that has been found to meet a prescribed standard of excellence. Certification in the United States began in 1914 largely in response to a demand for seed containing less mosaic and leaf roll. The volume of certified seed produced in 1947 approximated 44 million bushels in the United States and 11 million bushels in Canada. Coincident with the increase in volume has come an improvement in the standard of excellence and a decrease in the tolerance on diseases. As an example, the maximum tolerances in the New York certified-seed standard for 1948 were as follows at the second field inspection: for mosaic, 1 per cent; for leaf roll, 1 per cent; for spindle tuber, 1 per cent; for all three of those, 3 per cent; for yellow dwarf, 1 per cent; for purple top, 10 per cent; for Fusarium wilt, 1 per cent; for varietal mixture, 0.5 per cent; and for bacterial ring rot, 0 per cent. One of the principal benefits of seed certification is that it has established an interstate trade through which the buyer may with confidence purchase seed relatively free from those seed-borne diseases that are evident only in the growing plant.

The conditions under which seed is grown sometimes influence its quality. This is true to the extent that environment ultimately affects the spread of virus disease, maturity, sprout condition at planting time, and perhaps other conditions. Although muck-grown potatoes are sometimes used for seed, growers using such soils more often buy new seed at least every other year. Muck-grown seed is as good as that grown on upland soil provided it contains no more virus disease. However, the fact that foliage growth on muck is usually more prolific makes the control of disease vectors more difficult. This is especially true of aphids, spreaders of mosaic and leaf roll. With the introduction of DDT, the control of all potato insects has become less difficult.

Any evidence that seed grown under straw mulch is superior to unmulched stock does not appear conclusive. The fact that potatoes grown under mulch may yield more in response to a cooler, more moist soil, does not necessarily ensure greater vigor or less disease. when the crop is used for seed.

At one time, it appeared that potatoes grown under irrigation were not as satisfactory for seed as those grown under dry-land conditions. Comparative yield tests in the irrigated areas of the West often showed in favor of dry-land seed. More recently it has been shown that these differences were due to the greater incidence of virus disease in the seed grown under irrigation, and that the spread of spindle tuber and leaf roll is favored by such conditions. The conclusion now is that, apart from the disease factor, there is no difference in seed value between irrigated and dry-land grown seed potatoes.

Storage

Good storage of seed requires that it be maintained in good physical condition, and that it be in such sprouting condition at planting time that it will emerge quickly and produce sturdy plants. Temperatures above 40° F. and excessively high humidity in storage are conditions favorable to sprout formation. Temperatures kept constantly below 40° and a relative humidity of 80 to 90 per cent should maintain dormancy and prevent much shrinkage. Smith (1937) studied the effects of various storage temperatures and high and low humidities on yield and sprout development in both Irish Cobbler and Rural seed. Plants from tubers stored in constant-temperature, cold storage rooms at 50°, 40°, 35°, and 32° appeared above ground in that order. As temperature of storage increased, number of stems per plant, total number of tubers per plant, and number of No. 1 size tubers increased. Low humidity of storage resulted in the lowest number but in the longest individual sprouts. Similarly Hartman (1934), using Green Mountain seed potatoes, compared constant-storage temperatures of 50°, 40°, 35°, and 32° in their relation to date of planting, time of emergence, length of life of the plant, numbers of stems and tubers per plant, and yield. In that experiment, whole tubers were planted without desprouting, and replicated plantings were made on May 25, June 12, and July 7 at Ithaca, New York. Results from the May 25 or recommended planting date are summarized in table 29.

Largely because the seed stored at the 50° temperature had the most advanced sprout condition at planting time, it resulted in the earliest come-up, the longest life of plant, the fewest stalks and tubers per plant, and the highest total yield. When he planted similar lots of seed from each storage temperature on June 12 and on July 7, Hartman obtained the best yields from seed stored at 40° F. In general, the results from later planting were: less time

TABLE 29. EFFECTS OF STORAGE TEMPERATURE ON PROPAGA-
TION VALUE OF STORED GREEN MOUNTAIN SEED POTATOES.

Storage Temperature	Number of Days to Emerge	Number of Days of Live Foliage	Number of Stalks per Plant	Number of Tubers per Plant	Total Yield per Acre (Bushels)
50° F	11.8	102	2.0	7.5	458
40° F	22.5	98	2.4	8.9	412
35° F	26.1	95	2.8	9.0	389
32° F	28.5	93	3.4	9.4	351

needed to emerge, shorter-lived plants, more stalks and tubers per plant, and lower yields. One should conclude from this carefully conducted experiment that, as the planting date is delayed, the best storage temperature for the seed is lowered.

In the sequence of steps in handling seed potatoes after removal from storage, desprouting should come first. If the sprouts are so long as to interfere with feeding through the machine planter, or if the seed is to be chemically disinfested (treated), they should be removed. Otherwise the treatment is likely to kill them, and the adhering dead sprouts may retard growth of the next generation. Ordinarily the desprouting of seed potatoes is neither economical nor justified.

Seed Treatment

The purpose of seed treatment is to kill all surface-borne, disease-producing organisms. It is not effective against diseases borne internally. Among the diseases most commonly found on the surface skin of potato tubers are common scab, rhizoctonia or black scurf, wilt, blackleg and bacterial ring rot. Two facts should be considered in deciding whether to disinfest any lot of seed potatoes: (1) since both labor and materials are involved in the cost, treatment should be applied only when and to the extent that one or more of the above diseases are present, (2) seed treatment does not protect against disease present in the soil or ensure a crop of clean tubers; its value lies principally in killing diseases which, if introduced with the seed, would result in a poor stand of plants or infest an otherwise clean soil. Highly infectious diseases such as bacterial ring rot, blackleg, and spindle tuber may be spread by the knife used in cutting seed. Seed treatment before cutting is therefore a means of partial prevention of disease spread in this way.

Failure to get a crop of scab-free tubers after seed treatment has caused many growers to lose faith in the practice. This is because they do not realize that the scab organism is always active in a soil of favorable pH range, and because they do not understand the real function of seed treatment.

Fig. 22. Well-greened and ungreened seed pieces.

The methods and materials used in seed treatment are several. Most methods involve the use of either mercury preparations or formaldehyde. The mercurials most used have included corrosive sublimate, calomel, yellow oxide of mercury, and Semesan-Bel. Since the results from these have not been greatly different, the choice between them is in cost and convenience. In some states, the addition of an acid to increase effectiveness has been recommended. There is some evidence that where scab in the soil is a problem, formaldehyde rather than a mercurial should be used, because treatment with the latter seems to aggravate the disease. A hot formaldehyde solution is often used to shorten the period of immersion and to reduce the cost when a large volume of seed is to be treated in a short time. Depending on the material, the temperature, and the concentration, the treatment may be either a soak or a dip. For most diseases and treatments, the seed should be treated before cutting. Recently the rot of seed pieces by the Fusarium organism has become so serious on Long Island that treatment of the cut seed is recommended and generally practiced. Disinfesting of the seed-cutting knife is also sometimes recommended when highly infectious bacterial-disease organisms such as bacterial ring rot and blackleg are present.

Greensprouting

Whether or not seed potatoes are disinfested, it is usually advantageous to bring them out of storage at least a week before planting. Exposing the uncut tubers to indirect sunlight for a period of a week or longer causes the formation of tough, thickened, green sprouts. The practice is known as greensprouting, and the effect on the quality of sprouts and subsequent plant growth is beneficial.

Fig. 23. Exposing partially filled crates of seed potatoes in a staggered arrangement and in a protected place for greening.

In greening small lots, the seed can be spread in a shallow layer over a barn floor. For large quantities, a more practical method is to pile the partially filled crates in offset or staggered fashion so that most of the tubers will be exposed to the light (see figure 23). Exposure for a period of 1 to 3 weeks is sufficient. To the extent that greensprouted seed results in an earlier emergence and greater resistance to sprout injury from rhizoctonia, the stand of plants and yields are improved. The effect on multiple sprouting depends on whether the seed was dormant at the time of exposure. Exposure early when the seed is dormant usually results in a lower average number of stems per seed piece than does greening at a later date. The effect is essentially due to a difference in age of seed at time of planting. The benefits from greening seed are especially great when early planting and early emergence result in an earlier maturing crop. A test at Cornell in 1944, with Green Mountain variety, comparing seed greened 3 weeks with seed left in cellar storage until the day before planting showed that the greened seed had 23 per cent more plants over 4 inches tall 4 weeks after planting. The immediate effect of greensprouting is to produce foreshortened sprouts with shorter internodes and more nodes from which stolons and tubers can develop. Hardenburg (1935) in a 4-year experiment at the Cornell Agricultural Experiment Station obtained an earlier come-up from the greened seed and a yield increase of 17 bushels of No. 1 tubers to the acre. The effect of greening on habit of growth of the plant and on yield are summarized in table 30. Although greensprouting is more widely practiced in Europe than in America, it is gradually increasing in this country.

TABLE 30. EFFECT OF GREENSPROUTING ON GROWTH AND YIELD OF POTATOES.

Treatment	No. of Stems per Plant	No. of Stolons per Plant	No. of Tubers per Stem	No. 1 Yield per Acre (Bushels)
Greened	2.72	21.3	3.23	241
Not greened	3.33	16.3	2.79	224

Cutting Seed

Most seed tubers are cut into pieces because it is not economical to plant them whole. Cut seed is not better than whole from the standpoint of yield, and, besides, cutting not only involves an additional labor cost but also makes the seed more subject to drying out and to the invasion of rot-producing organisms. When small tubers are not the result of seed-borne diseases, they yield as well as cut pieces from large tubers from the same plant. When small, whole tubers can be purchased as certified seed they are worth some premium over large tubers.

Many experiments have been made to compare the efficiency of different sizes of seed pieces. The results have very generally indicated that yield increases as size of piece increases. Such tests do not indicate, nevertheless, that large pieces represent the most efficient use of seed. While comparing large with small pieces, if all sizes are spaced the same, much more seed is required when large pieces are

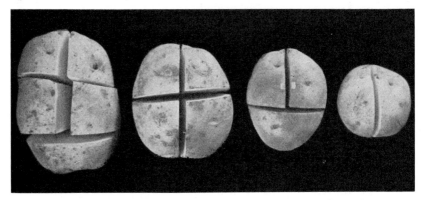

Fig. 24. Cutting Sebago seed according to size of tuber. Note right-angle cuts and division of seed ends for blocky pieces and equality of eye numbers. *Left to right:* tubers weigh 8, 6, 4, and 2 ounces.

used. Therefore, when comparing different sizes, it seems more fair to vary the spacing according to size of piece and thereby keep the amount of seed planted constant. This relationship was shown by Sprague and Evaul (1929) of New Jersey, with results as indicated in tables 31 and 32.

TABLE 31. RELATION OF AMOUNT OF SEED TO YIELD OF GREEN MOUNTAIN POTATOES (PIECES SPACED 9 INCHES APART).*

Size of Pieces (Ounces)	Seed per Acre (Bushels)	Total Yield (Bushels)	Total Yield Minus Seed (Bushels)	Total Yield per Bushel of Seed (Bushels)
½	11	147	136	13.4
1	22	168	146	7.6
1½	33	188	155	5.7

* Average 1924–1926. Adapted from Sprague and Evaul (1929).

These data show clearly that (1) as size of piece increases from ½ ounce to 1½ ounces, yield increases as amount of seed per acre increases, (2) when amount of seed per acre is constant, pieces as small as 1 ounce not only give as much yield as larger pieces but also result in more yield per bushel of seed planted. Tubers smaller than 1 inch in diameter or weighing less than 1 ounce are not usually safe to use, because of the danger of drying out or failure to produce

TABLE 32. RELATION OF SIZE OF SEED PIECE TO YIELD OF GREEN MOUNTAIN POTATOES.*

Size of Piece (Ounces)	Spacing in Row (Inches)	Total Yield (Bushels)	Total Yield Minus Seed (Bushels)	Total Yield per Bushel of Seed (Bushels)
½	7.5	144	131	10.9
1	15.0	145	132	11.0
1½	22.5	121	108	9.2

* Average 1924–1926; 13.2 bushels of seed per acre. Adapted from Sprague and Evaul (1929).

a good sprout. Varieties with comparatively few eyes require larger pieces and more bushels of seed to each acre than those with many eyes. Therefore, more seed per acre of Katahdin, Chippewa, Sebago, and Mohawk is necessary than of Green Mountain, Russet Burbank, and Irish Cobbler.

Chucka and Steinmetz (1945) compared the yield from different sizes of tubers, both whole and cut, of the Green Mountain, Katahdin, and Sebago varieties. Their results averaged for the three varieties are shown in table 33.

TABLE 33. RELATION OF SIZE OF SEED TUBER AND SEED PIECE TO YIELD.

Size of Seed Tuber (Inches)	Size of Seed Piece (Ounces)	Yield per Acre, Average 3 Varieties (Bushels)
1 to 1¼ whole	0.54	281
1¼ to 1½ whole	0.94	320
1½ to 1 11/16 whole	1.39	326
1 11/16 to 1⅞ whole	1.76	341
1 11/16 to 1⅞ split	0.90	304
1⅞ to 2½ split	0.93	282
1⅞ to 2½ split	1.43	319
1⅞ to 2½ split	1.92	349
Least significant difference at 5% level or odds 19:1		23.2
Least significant difference at 1% level or odds 99:1		30.2

These workers concluded that (1) yield increased as size of piece increased for both whole and cut seed, (2) whole seed gave somewhat higher yield than cut seed for pieces of similar weight, (3) number of stalks per plant and number of tubers per hill increased as size of piece increased, and (4) there were more oversize tubers on plants from the smallest seed pieces.

Apparently the minimum size of potato seed piece is that which provides sufficient substance for the plant to establish its root system. Ordinarily, that is when the plant is about 10 inches tall and has been planted about 6 weeks. Denny (1929) established this fact by careful amputation of the mother seed piece from Cobbler and Triumph varieties at various stages of development. Removing the seed piece when the plants were just up or 22 days from planting gave yields only ⅓ those of the checks. Amputation a week later gave yields about 80 per cent of the checks, while removal just 42 days from planting resulted in yields about equal to that of the check plants. Denny concluded that, 6 weeks after planting, the mother tuber served no further useful role.

The best method of cutting seed is that which is quickest, which gives blocky pieces, and which results in a minimum of cut surface. Square rather than diagonal cuts are desirable; unless the tuber is distinctly elongated, it is always best to split the apical end to equalize the number and vigor of eyes and buds. Tubers large enough to justify only one cut should be cut longitudinally rather than transversely. Cutting according to size of tuber is illustrated in figure 24. Since cutting tends to eliminate apical dominance, if a tuber is cut while still dormant the eyes on each piece usually develop at the same rate, and the result is a uniform stand of plants. If a tuber is already sprouted at the apical end, cutting it transversely will result in an earlier emergence from the apical end pieces.

Stewart (1936) compared apical and basal halves of equal-sized tubers both before and after the apical sprouts had started. When cut after sprouting, the apical seed halves significantly outyielded the plants from the basal halves. Cut before sprouting, there was no difference in yield.

The use of machine cutters is practical when large quantities are to be cut in a short time, but it naturally results in some waste in blank or eyeless pieces.

The number of bushels of seed required per acre varies with the variety and the moisture and fertility of the soil. Varieties with few eyes, like Katahdin and Sequoia, especially if the tubers are large, require the most seed. The seed requirement is greater and more costly today than formerly when varieties with more eyes

Fig. 25. An efficient arrangement for cutting seed by pushing tuber against stationary knife.

were grown. In general, the rate of planting can be increased profitably as the fertility level increases, and as irrigation water is available. The amount of seed necessary to plant an acre naturally varies with size of seed piece, width of rows, and spacing in the row. Within the limits of usual practice, seed requirement is shown in table 34.

Curing Seed

When fresh-cut seed is stored several days, or when it is planted in either cold-wet or hot-dry soil, it sometimes rots or dries excessively. If it can be planted soon after cutting in an ideal seedbed there is probably no advantage in curing it. By curing is meant the formation of a callus or wound periderm layer over the cut surface. Cured seed is less perishable by virtue of a protective layer of woody tissue which forms within a few hours, if atmospheric

conditions are favorable. Conditions favoring curing are relatively
high temperature and high humidity, or those that prevent rapid
drying of the cut surface. Most rapid curing results when the temperature ranges from 60° to 70° F., and the humidity is at least 90
per cent.

Artschwager (1927) studied the physiology of curing of cut seed
and reported two essential processes. First is the suberization or
oxidation and coagulation of fatty acids in the sap which exudes

TABLE 34. RELATION OF SIZE OF SEED PIECE AND PLANT SPACING
TO NUMBER OF BUSHELS OF SEED REQUIRED TO PLANT
AN ACRE.

Spacing, in Inches		Bushels of Seed Required to the Acre, According to Following Sizes of Seed Pieces			
Rows	Seed Pieces	½-ounce	1-ounce	1½-ounce	2-ounce
32	8	12.8	25.5	38.3	51.1
	10	10.2	20.4	30.6	40.8
	12	8.5	17.0	25.6	34.0
	14	7.3	14.6	21.9	29.2
34	8	12.0	24.0	36.0	48.0
	10	9.6	19.2	28.8	38.4
	12	8.0	16.0	24.0	32.0
	14	6.9	13.7	20.6	27.4
36	8	11.3	22.7	34.0	45.4
	10	9.1	18.1	27.2	36.3
	12	7.6	15.1	22.7	30.2
	14	6.5	13.0	19.4	25.9

after cutting. If suberization is complete, the resulting suberin layer
completely seals over the cut surface. This is necessary before the
wound periderm or layers of woody tissue can form beneath. In
other words, the suberin layer must form first on the surface, after
which the callus or wound periderm forms beneath. That the rate
of curing depends on temperature was well shown by Artschwager
in data summarized in table 35.

TABLE 35. RELATION OF TEMPERATURE TO RATE OF CURING OF CUT SEED POTATOES (FROM ARTSCHWAGER).

Variety	Temperature		Days Needed after Cutting for Layers to Form	
	°F.	°C.	Suberin	Wound Periderm
Cobbler	5	41.0	5	—
	10	50.0	3	4
	15	69.8	1	2
Russet Rural	5	41.0	8	—
	10	50.0	3	6
	15	69.8	1	2

In the above study, cut seed held for 6 days at 12° C. (53.6° F.) showed a marked difference in rate of curing as affected by relative humidity. At 64 per cent humidity wound periderm formation had been barely initiated, at 74 per cent 1½ layers had been formed, and at 94 per cent 2 layers.

It is not always easy to provide conditions for rapid curing on the farm. In early spring, it may be necessary to use an electric heater or an oil stove to provide the proper temperature. Close attention to keeping the temperature from going above 70° F. is advised. The cut seed may well be held in slatted crates, partially filled and piled in a staggered fashion to allow good aeration. An electric fan to keep the air moving and the temperature uniform is sometimes used. To provide high humidity, burlap sacks soaked in water may be thrown over the crates of cut seed for 3 to 5 days until suberization is complete. These bags should be removed soon to prevent heating and the development of molds.

Dusting Cut Seed

The practice of dusting cut seed to prevent "bleeding" is no longer advised. Formerly such driers as land plaster or gypsum, hydrated lime, and sulfur were used. This practice is now known to prevent curing as it prevents suberization through rapid drying. Dusting of cut seed, contrary to its expressed purpose, does not prevent shrinkage during storage.

REFERENCES

Appleman, Charles O. Study of rest period in potato tubers. Md. Agr. Exp. Sta. Bul. 183, 1914.

Appleman, C. O. Potato sprouts as an index of seed value. Md. Agr. Exp. Sta. Bul. 265, 1924.

Appleman, C. O., and E. V. Miller. A chemical and physiological study of maturity in potatoes. Jour. Agr. Research 33, No. 6, Dec., 1926.

Artschwager, Ernst. Wound periderm formation in the potato as affected by temperature and humidity. Jour. Agr. Research 35, No. 11, Dec., 1927.

Bushnell, John. The normal multiple sprouting of seed potatoes. Ohio Agr. Exp. Sta. Bul. 430, 1929.

Chucka, Joseph A., and Ferdinand A. Steinmetz. Potatoes. Maine Agr. Exp. Sta. Bul. 438, 1945.

Denny, F. E. Hastening the sprouting of dormant potato tubers. Amer. Jour. Bot. 13, 118–125, 1926.

Denny, F. E. Role of mother tuber in growth of potato plant. Bot. Gaz. 87, No. 1, Feb., 1929.

Hardenburg, E. V. Greensprouting seed potatoes. Cornell Univ. Agr. Exp. Sta. Bul. 632, 1935.

Hartman, John D. Studies of the effects of storage temperature on the propagation value of potato tubers. Cornell Univ. Agr. Exp. Sta. Mem. 168, 1934.

Lombard, P. M. Effect of storage and repeated sprouting of seed potatoes on their growth and productiveness. U.S. Dept. Agr. Circ. 465, 1938.

Martin, William H. Report of Department of Plant Pathology. N.J. Agr. Exp. Sta., Year Ending June 30, 1921.

Smith, Ora. Influence of storage temperature and humidity on seed value of potatoes. Cornell Univ. Agr. Exp. Sta. Bul. 663, 1937.

Sprague, Howard B., and E. E. Evaul. Effect of size of seed piece and rate of planting on yields of white potatoes. Jour. Amer. Soc. Agron. 21, No. 5, May, 1929.

Stewart, F. C. The relative vigor and productivity of potato plants from basal and apical sets cut from tubers in different stages of sprouting. N.Y. State Agr. Exp. Sta. [Geneva] Bul. 658, 1936.

Stuart, William, and E. H. Milstead. Shortening the rest period of the potato. U.S. Dept. Agr. Tech. Bul. 415, 1934.

Werner, H. O. Further report on environmental relations to quality in seed potatoes. Potato Assn. Amer. Proc., 1926.

Westover, K. C. The effect on yield of sprout removal from potato seed tubers. Amer. Soc. Hort. Sci. Proc., 1928.

CHAPTER 7

Planting and Cultivation

SEVERAL of the factors that influence the yield and quality of the potato crop long before the actual planting operation has begun are discussed in previous chapters. Others of basic importance are choice of the field and preparation of the soil.

Choice of Field

Too many poorly adapted fields are used for potatoes merely because they seem to be required to carry out the scheme of crop rotation. This is especially true on dairy farms where it seems desirable to rotate potatoes with forage crops. If the number of fields really well adapted to potatoes is limited, however, it may be best either to use a separate rotation or to grow the crop a number of years on the same field.

In choosing the field, it is well to remember that the soil should be of loose, well-drained, friable structure to a depth of at least 12 inches. A soil reaction of pH 5.0 to 5.5 is preferable. If there is considerable variation in soil reaction among several fields available, potatoes should be planted on the more acid ones, and alfalfa, sweet clover, root crops, and other so-called high-lime crops on the fields of higher pH values. Choice of field should also take into account the danger of infestation with the wheat wireworm and grubs. These pests are most likely to be troublesome if the field is naturally wet, and if it has been in sod several years previously. Since the adult of the wheat wireworm lays its eggs generally in cool moist soil in early spring (May 1 to June 15 in upstate New York) it is safest not to plant in a field which was in sod or small-grain seeding during the previous two years.

Fitting the Soil

A potato seedbed is well prepared if all organic matter including strawy manure is uniformly incorporated throughout the plow furrow slice and well covered to ensure rapid decomposition. The seedbed should be uniformly fitted to a depth of at least 8 inches, because not only yield but also tuber shape and quality are influenced by its character. To overfit the surface layer and neglect

Fig. 26. An automatic, picker-type potato planter showing fertilizer hopper forward, seed hopper at rear, large opening discs in front, smaller covering discs at rear.

the lower part of the furrow slice is a mistake. On the heavier soils, this results in a crusting or ceiling of the surface, making it more difficult to control weeds and for the plants to emerge.

In fitting a field of newly plowed sod, especially on the heavier soils, the disc or cutaway harrow is appropriate. Dependence on a light spring-tooth or peg-tooth harrow in such cases is not good practice. Use of the land roller to compact newly plowed land may be desirable as a means of hastening the decomposition of organic matter, but its use should be followed just before planting by the use of a deep-fitting implement to loosen the soil. Fall plowing is preferable to spring plowing, if the soil is naturally wet or heavy, and if much coarse organic matter is to be turned down. Spring plowing is more feasible if the soil is light or loamy and subject to erosion. On the heavier soils, deep plowing to improve structure is desirable, but the danger of bringing up too much poorly oxidized subsoil at one time should be avoided.

Date of Planting

Mistakes made at planting time are usually costly and impossible to correct. Stand of plants, speed of emergence, injury from soil-borne disease organisms, seasonal problems with foliage insects, quality of crop, and yield are all influenced by time, depth, and method of planting.

Fig. 27. A 2-row, assisted-feed planter requiring an extra man to assure a more perfect stand of plants.

Actual date of planting best for any region depends on length of growing season available, time of year when the crop can be marketed to best advantage, and seasonal weather throughout the growth period. Only at high altitudes and in the northern parts

of the potato states bordering Canada is the growing season likely
to limit full maturity of the crop. Because cool temperatures favor
potato yields, regions affording such conditions get high yields in
spite of the fact that the short season prevents normal maturity.
To take advantage of a cool growing season, the main crop of potatoes grown in the South is planted in the fall. The best planting
date is that which provides cool, moist conditions when the plants
are blossoming and setting tubers and relatively short days late in
the season for maximum tuber development. Such conditions are
provided for most of the important potato areas in the northern
and northeastern states by planting between May 1 and June 15.
This gives long days for plant growth in the summer and shortening
days in the fall when the crop is maturing. It is possible to plant
earlier along the Atlantic seaboard where the climate is tempered
by the Atlantic Ocean.

In general the yield of potatoes varies directly with earliness of
planting. This was well illustrated by a 6-year date-of-planting experiment in Rhode Island made by Rich (1945), the results of which
are shown in table 36.

TABLE 36. RELATION OF DATE OF PLANTING TO YIELD AND
GRADE OF POTATOES.

Date Planted	Average Yield 1939–1944, incl. (Bushels per Acre)		
	Total	No. 1	Per Cent No. 1
April 25	309	278	90.0
May 5	286	252	88.1
May 15	258	213	82.5
May 25	221	173	78.3
Least difference for significance at odds of 19:1	19	29	——

These data indicate that a difference of 1 month in date of planting made an average difference of about 100 bushels to the acre
in yield of No. 1 grade potatoes, and that the percentage of No. 1
grade was also higher for the earlier planting date. Huckett (1935),
working at the Long Island Vegetable Research Farm, and also with
Green Mountain variety, got results very similar to those of Rich;

he found too that it was much easier to control foliage insects such as the Colorado beetle, leaf hopper, flea beetle, and aphis when planting was done early. Where length of growing season is not limited, the earliest possible planting date is not always the one most desirable. Little is gained by planting early in cold, poorly prepared soil. A warm moist soil favors quick emergence of plants, and under such conditions they should come up in about two weeks. Planting in cold soil usually results in a period of emergence of 4 weeks, sprout injury by rhizoctonia, seed-piece rot, and a poor stand.

Plant Spacing

Spacing of seed pieces in the row influences seed requirement, yield, and the average size of tubers in the crop. Spacing varies from 6 inches to 36 inches, and on the average it is much closer than in former years when much of the acreage was planted in check rows to facilitate cross cultivation. Experiments have repeatedly shown that close spacing is best, because it results in higher yields, a more uniform size of tuber, and less tendency to oversize and hollow heart. Growers who plant closest not only usually average a higher yield and require more seed to the acre, but they also get more yield for each bushel of seed planted. This is well shown by a survey of 157 farms in western New York in 1932, results of which are summarized in table 37.

TABLE 37. RELATION OF SEED SPACING TO YIELD ON 157 NEW YORK FARMS.

Seed Spaced (Inches)	Number of Farms	Seed per Acre (Bushels)	Average Total Yield per Acre (Bushels)	No. 1 Size (Per Cent)	Yield per Bushel of Seed (Bushels)
9–12	45	18.8	253	70	13.5
13–15	68	17.3	215	73	12.4
16–19	33	16.9	189	75	11.2
20–36	11	13.4	144	78	10.7
Avg. and totals	157	17.3	214	73	12.3

Since the adoption of varieties with relatively few eyes on the tuber, such as Sebago and Katahdin, it has become practical to use more seed and larger seed pieces. In 1943, Smith, Hommel, and Kelly (1943) published data showing that "with the Sebago and possibly others of the newer varieties, much larger yield responses are obtained from close spacing and the use of large seed-pieces than with the Rural and possibly other old standard varieties." These authors, comparing 11-inch with 14-inch spacing, got much higher yields with the 11-inch for Sebago but practically no difference for Rural.

Fig. 28. Much time is saved by servicing the planter with seed and fertilizer at the end of the field.

Seed planted late, being less apically dominant, should be spaced wider than seed planted early. Bushnell (1930) found 9-inch spacing superior to 12-inch spacing for his early plantings, while for three later plantings of the same seed there was no difference. He also compared 6-, 9-, and 12-inch spacings for seed treated for various periods of time with thiourea to induce multiple sprouting. The 12-inch spacing was best for seed soaked 12 hours, while 6-inch spacing gave best yields for the same seed when untreated. Edmundson (1935) compared spacings of 8, 10, 12, and 14 inches for both the Rural New Yorker No. 2 and the Triumph varieties. Yields of tubers weighing 3 to 12 ounces increased as spacing decreased. Yields of tubers weighing 16 ounces or more and of tubers affected with second-growth and hollow heart increased as the spacing increased.

With the increased use of irrigation water and larger amounts of fertilizer has come the question of the relation of seed spacing to these factors. Usually closer spacing is better justified when the fertility level is high and soil moisture ample than where they are limited. As recently as 1944 this fact was demonstrated by an experiment with Katahdin variety at the New Jersey Experiment Station. Results are given in table 38.

TABLE 38. RELATION OF FERTILITY LEVEL AND IRRIGATION TO PLANT SPACING AND YIELD.

Fertilizer per Acre (Pounds)	Plant Spacing (Inches)	Total Yield per Acre (Bushels)		
		Irrigated	Not Irrigated	Difference
1200	8	274	182	92
	10	250	171	79
	12	238	174	64
1600	8	283	188	95
	10	260	183	77
	12	239	159	80
2000	8	274	155	119
	10	246	149	97
	12	239	149	90

These data indicate that the 8-inch spacing was better than either 10- or 12-inch so long as not less than 1200 pounds of fertilizer was used, and regardless of whether the crop was irrigated. They also indicate that irrigation was more effective in increasing yield at the 8-inch spacing than at the wider spacings.

Optimum spacing should and probably does vary according to the habit of growth of the variety. Early-maturing, small-plant varieties require less space than do varieties producing big plants. Whether this fact applies to spacing closer than 12 inches is debatable. A comparison of 6-, 9-, and 12-inch spacings for 8 varieties was made by Chucka, Hawkins, and Brown (1944). Their results at Presque Isle, Maine, are summarized in table 39.

TABLE 39. RELATION OF VARIETY TO SPACING OF SEED AND
YIELD.

Variety	Yield of No. 1 Size Potatoes in Barrels per Acre			
	6 Inches	9 Inches	12 Inches	Average
Cobbler	94	105	103	101
Warba	122	118	113	118
Chippewa	121	128	128	126
Houma	116	114	118	116
Katahdin	126	123	119	123
Green Mt.	127	129	129	128
Sebago	128	133	126	129
Earlaine No. 2	129	140	146	138
Average	120	124	123	—

As shown by the yields recorded here, there is little indication that spacing closer than 12 inches in the row is profitable, especially because of the extra seed required for the closer spacing. This appears to be true for all of the varieties tested in this experiment.

Depth of Planting

The depth at which the potato seed piece is planted naturally varies with soil type and the method or equipment used in planting. Planting is usually shallower in heavy soil and when hand methods are used than when the soil is light and machine planters are available. Depth of planting affects speed of emergence of the plant, depth at which the tubers form, the need for ridge culture, the incidence of sunburn injury, ease of digging, and yield. Zavitz (1916) planted potatoes at 1-, 3-, 5-, and 7-inch depths and found that when planted 2 inches deep or less the tubers formed at a depth deeper than the seed was planted. When planted 5 inches deep or more, the tubers formed at a depth shallower than the seed was planted. So it appears that even though tubers tend to develop at the 3- to 4-inch depth, this depth is influenced by depth of planting. Potato growers generally realize that deep planting makes harder digging and sometimes plant so shallow as to limit yields, increase sunburn injury, and necessitate ridge culture. Depending on type of soil, 3 to 4 inches is generally the best planting depth. Hardenburg (1935), comparing 2-, 4-, and 6-inch depths for both Green

Mountain and Rural varieties planted in a rather heavy silt loam soil, found that 15 days after planting about 15 per cent more plants had emerged from the 2-inch than from the 6-inch depth of planting. The average yield and number of stems per plant for both varieties over the 4-year period (1928–1931) are shown in table 40.

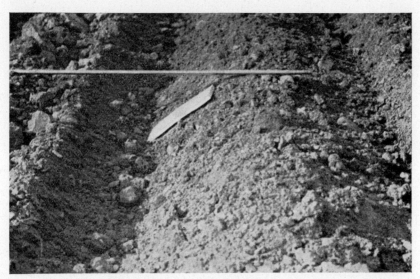

Fig. 29. A 6-inch ridge left by the potato planter covers the seed too deep and encourages extreme ridging later.

Although the average number of stems per plant was significantly higher for the 2-inch than for the 4-inch depth, the number was not reduced by planting deeper than 4 inches. Yields were about the same for the 2- and the 4-inch planting depths. Yields were reduced by planting at 6 inches in both 1929 and 1930 when rainfall was normal; they increased in 1931 when the season was excep-

TABLE 40. EFFECT OF DEPTH OF PLANTING ON STEM NUMBER AND YIELD.

Depth Planted (Inches)	Average Number of Stems per Plant	Average No. 1 Yield per Acre (Bushels)
2	3.07	238.4
4	2.89	242.0
6	2.93	230.0

tionally dry. This again indicates that planting should be deeper in soils subject to quick drying and in regions of relatively low rainfall.

When seed is planted deeply to provide ample soil moisture for root and tuber development, if the seed piece is covered too deeply it may emerge very slowly. This can be avoided by a recommended system known as the deep-plant, shallow-cover method as illustrated in figure 30. Deep planting without deep covering is desirable and can be done by equipping the planter with large discs in front to open the furrow and smaller discs behind to cover the seed. By widening the space between the rear discs and lessening the angle at which they are set, the seed will be covered shallowly and the furrow not completely filled, as shown in figure 30, lower. This system encourages rapid growth by warming the soil over the seed piece and by not lessening aeration with too deep covering. At the first cultivation, the furrow is filled, and weeds which have started since planting will be covered. This system avoids the necessity of excessive ridging as in the case of figure 30, upper.

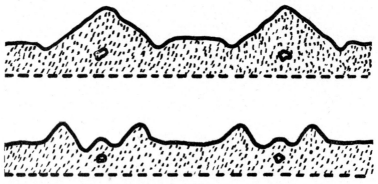

Fig. 30. Deep-plant, shallow-cover method of potato planting. *Upper:* ordinary covering. *Lower:* shallow covering.

Planting Equipment

Most of the commercial crop is now planted with machine or automatic planters which open the furrow with discs, distribute the fertilizer in bands on either side of and a little below the level of the seed piece, drop the seed through a separate tube, and partially or wholly fill the furrow with a rear pair of covering discs. These planters are of two principal types—one the picker type, the other the platform type. The latter provides pockets rotating over a horizontal disc or platform to ensure even spacing and a more perfect stand; it requires an extra man to sit behind the platform to see that one and only one seed piece is delivered into the planter tube from each slot or compartment. The platform type gives a more even and a more perfect stand than the picker type, but, with man labor expensive, fewer growers than formerly use it. With closer spacing, an occasional skip by the picker type is not serious. There is probably some spread of such diseases as black leg, bacterial ringrot, and spindle tuber by infection from the picker points of this type of planter, but no convenient method of prevention has yet been devised. Spacing of seed pieces is regulated by a change of sprockets, which in turn changes the speed of rotation of the picker points. Modern planters in use by large operators are equipped to plant two, three, or four rows at a time. For maximum efficiency, these planters are serviced with seed and fertilizer from a motor truck at the end of each field. Small plantings of 1 or 2 acres are usually planted by hand after the furrows are opened with a shovel plow or middlebuster, and the fertilizer is strung in the furrow and brushed or cultivated in. Covering of the seed in such cases is readily done with a disc coverer or ridging hoe.

Contour Planting and Strip Cropping

An increasing proportion of our potato acreage is on soil that is easily eroded by surface water. Some of it in New York and Pennsylvania is on land which slopes 5 to 20 per cent. Heavy rains, flash floods particularly, result annually in the loss of much topsoil by washing and the loss of both fertilizer and seed. If such losses are to be prevented and permanence for a profitable potato industry is to be obtained, appropriate soil conservation measures must be practiced. This is as true in the comparatively level areas along the Atlantic seaboard as on the hillier farms farther inland. In contour planting, erosion is checked by so plowing and planting that each row of potatoes is horizontal or level with the slope of the land. Where a level is not available to lay out the contours, the rows should be at least crosswise of the slope. On the steeper fields in many hilly areas, strip cropping is an appropriate way to check erosion. By this method strips of sod crops or small grains about 10 rods wide are planted between similar strips of potatoes.

Tillage and Weed Control

Although weeds are a problem in growing potatoes, they are probably less so than in growing corn, beans, and most other vegetables. If the potatoes are not planted on a weedy seedbed or old sod land, and if the soil is well prepared, two or three cultivations should be sufficient to control weeds. After the plants are well established, and the first crop of weed seedlings is destroyed, the potato plants shade the ground sufficiently to keep later weeds in check. Perennial grasses such as quack grass and nut grass, however, are especially difficult to control.

Fig. 31. A 12-foot weeder is ideal to control weeds after planting and until potato plants are several inches tall.

The primary purpose of tillage is weed control. Beyond that there seems to be no profit in cultivating except to break any crust formed by heavy rains so that surface water can be readily absorbed. Much damage has been done to the plant root system and needless expense has been incurred by late-season cultivation. By the time the potato plant has blossomed, its system of fine, fibrous roots interlace between the rows close to the surface, and even the most shallow cultivation will damage it. The extent of this surface root system is illustrated in figure 32. To determine, in terms of reduced yield, the extent of damage to the root system by root pruning such as would result from cultivation, Moore (1937) compared results from merely scraping the surface soil to control weeds with those from cutting of the roots 4 inches away from the plants with a spade. His results are shown in table 41.

TABLE 41. EFFECT OF ROOT PRUNING ON YIELD OF POTATOES.

Treatment	Fresh Weight of Tops (Ounces)	Number of Tubers per Plant	Average Yield per Acre (Bushels)	
			Total	No. 1
Planted 4 inches deep, scraped (no cultivation)	18.6	6.8	484	467
Planted 4 inches deep, roots pruned 4" from plant	10.9	6.5	408	384
Difference	7.7	0.3	76	83

The potato plant itself is not so easily injured by tillage implements as most other cultivated crops. For this reason most of the control of weeds should be done just before and for a period of two or three weeks after the plant emerges. A wide-sweep implement, such as the weeder with flexible teeth resembling those of a hay rake, is both efficient and economical for the purpose. It covers many rows at each sweep, does not dig deeply, and removes weeds in as well as between the rows. It can be used safely until the plants are at least 6 inches tall.

Control of weeds by chemicals has been tried recently and with considerable promise. Pre-emergence spray applications have been most used. Applied to the surface soil just before the potato plants emerge and 7 to 10 days after planting, most of the weeds that have germinated are destroyed. This means that little or no cultivation is necessary afterward.

Ridge versus Level Culture

From the beginning of potato production it has been customary to speak of a "hill" of potatoes. The expression derives from the fact that when labor was cheap and all work was done either by hand or with horses, the seed pieces were spaced widely, and a mound of soil was built around each plant. The reason for wide spacing was cross cultivation and easy weed control. The reason for the very general practice of ridging the rows was to make digging easier and to keep the newly developing tubers covered for protection against sunburn and freezing injury. Ridging or building soil against the row is still practiced to some extent in the more humid and hillier potato regions throughout the East and South.

Fig. 32. Soil removed to show potato surface root system about 95 days after planting. These are unpruned roots in top 3 inches of soil, indicating injury likely to result from excess cultivation. (Vegetable Crops Dept., Cornell Univ.)

The type of ridge used in Aroostook County, Maine, in other New England states, and in northern New York is rather extreme in that it is steep, narrow, and high. Ridging to a slight extent is the natural result of cultivating soil toward the row to cover weeds and to keep the tubers covered. On the heavier soils and in the hilly areas, especially where rainfall is high, moderate ridging of the proper type is probably justified. A low broad ridge, if any, is advised, because it results in a minimum of root injury and unnecessary drying of the soil. Such a ridge can be built by narrowing the cultivator teeth before each successive cultivation. A broad, flat-topped ridge also allows more rain water to be absorbed at a time when the enlarging plant most needs it. Extreme ridging as habitually practiced by many growers results in root injury, drying of the soil at a critical time, and a reduction in yield. This fact was well demonstrated by Moore (1937) who compared level culture with 4-inch and 7-inch ridging on both heavy silt loam and sandy loam soils at Ithaca, New York. His results are summarized in tables 42 and 43.

TABLE 42. EFFECT OF RIDGING ON YIELD IN DUNKIRK SILT LOAM SOIL.

Depth Planted (Inches)	Cultivation	Total Yield per Acre (Bushels)		
		1933	1934	Average
4	Level	327	270	299
1	4-inch ridge	302	276	289
1	7-inch ridge	287	255	271

Although the difference in yield between the level and the 4-inch ridge type of cultivation was not statistically significant, the yield from the 7-inch ridge cultivation was significantly lower than that from the level cultivation. Extreme ridging in this experiment resulted not only in root pruning but also in considerably more loss of soil moisture. Moore made a similar comparison, under both irrigated and unirrigated conditions, on a sandy loam soil in 1934 (table 43).

TABLE 43. EFFECT OF RIDGING ON YIELD IN IRRIGATED AND UN-IRRIGATED SANDY LOAM SOIL.

Depth Planted (Inches)	Cultivation	Total Yield per Acre (Bushels)		
		Irrigated	Not Irrigated	Difference
4	Level	424	386	38
1	4-inch ridge	414	345	69
1	7-inch ridge	426	337	89

The data in table 43 show that under irrigation, or when soil water is not a limiting factor, ridging is less likely to reduce yields than it is when water is limited by lack of irrigation. They also show that extreme ridging is more likely to reduce potato yields when soil moisture is limited than is level cultivation.

The effect of ridging on the incidence of sunburn, second-growth, and misshaped tubers is not well known. A field survey of 158 New York farms, made in 1932, comparing ridges varying from 2.5 to 9.0 inches in height indicated less sunburn injury for the higher ridges but no relation to second-growth and misshaped tubers.

Fig. 33. Vertical profile showing root distribution about 54 days after planting. Seed planted deep with shallow covering, surface-scraped only. (Vegetable Crops Dept., Cornell Univ.)

Straw Mulching

Surface mulching with straw, paper, leaves, and other material has been used on potatoes to check weed growth, maintain soil moisture, and reduce soil temperature but only to a very limited extent. The labor cost of applying and removing the mulch apparently has been such that the benefits have not justified the practice. Mulching as a field practice has been done to a limited extent in southern Ohio and in western Nebraska where soil temperatures are normally high and moisture is sometimes limited.

Bushnell and Welton (1931) compared straw mulch with ordinary cultivation over a 5-year period at Wooster and in southern Ohio. The straw was applied at a depth of 8 to 10 inches soon after planting, the amount varying from 4 to 10 tons. The larger applications of straw gave somewhat better results than the smaller amounts in the years when rainfall was below normal. In 1925, a dry year, the mulched plots gave a yield about double that of the cultivated plots. In 1926, when rainfall was above normal, mulching decreased the yield. Again in 1927, another dry year, mulching gave somewhat larger yields than cultivation. In 1928 and 1929, 10 tons of straw mulch were applied at three different dates, namely about April 1 at planting time, in early May when the plants had emerged, and in early June when the potatoes were in blossom. Lowest yields resulted when the straw was applied at planting time, best yields when it was applied just after the plants had come up. These authors concluded that (1) even with ample rainfall the mulch maintained a lower soil temperature, which in that location is normally too high, and (2) applied too early the mulch retarded growth and decreased nitrification so that the leaves showed evidence of nitrogen deficiency. Apparently any kind of surface mulch as a substitute for cultivation can justify the cost of labor and materials only in situations where soil moisture is deficient, the soil is light, and summer temperatures high.

REFERENCES

Bushnell, John. Rate of planting potatoes with some reference to sprouting habit and size of plants. Ohio Agr. Exp. Sta. Bul. 462, 1930.

Bushnell, John, and F. A. Welton. Some effect of straw mulch on yield of potatoes. Jour. Agr. Research 43, No. 9, 1931.

Chucka, Joseph A., Arthur Hawkins, and Bailey E. Brown. Potatoes. Maine Agr. Exp. Sta. Bul. 426, pp. 252–253, 1944.

Edmundson, W. C. Distance of planting Rural New Yorker No. 2 and Triumph potatoes as affecting yield, hollow heart, growth cracks and second-growth tubers. U.S. Dept. Agr. Circ. 338, 1935.

Hardenburg, E. V. Greensprouting seed potatoes. Cornell Univ. Agr. Exp. Sta. Bul. 632, 1935.

Huckett, H. C. Planting dates as an aid to potato insect control on Long Island, N.Y. State Agr. Exp. Sta. [Geneva] Bul. 652, 1935.

Moore, George C. Soil and plant response to certain methods of potato cultivation. Cornell Univ. Agr. Exp. Sta. Bul. 662, 1937.

Rich, A. E. Some factors affecting the yield and grade of Green Mountain potatoes in Rhode Island. R.I. Agr. Exp. Sta. Bul. 297, 1945.

Smith, Ora, R. F. Hommel, and W. C. Kelly. Relation of rate and placement of fertilizer, variety, seed spacing, and size of seed-piece to yields of potatoes. Amer. Potato Jour., 20, No. 10, 1943.

Zavitz, C. A. Potatoes. Ontario Dept. Agr. Bul. 239, 1916.

CHAPTER 8

Varieties

IT IS IMPOSSIBLE to say how many varieties of potatoes there are in the United States at any particular time. This is because many names are of local application, many new names are coined every year, and some names are merely synonyms of other varieties. In addition, no one organization is responsible for officially cataloging even recognized varieties, and, after all, the term variety is variously defined.

Definition

To prevent the mere naming of potatoes without regard to origin the term variety should be defined. A variety is a heritably distinct type within a species. Applying this definition, not only morphological characters but also such heritably distinct characters as yield, disease and insect resistance, heat tolerance, length of rest period, and frost resistance justify the application of a variety name. Even so, certain old varieties such as Rural New Yorker No. 2, Carman No. 3, and Sir Walter Raleigh, quite indistinct morphologically, were rightly given different names because they are known to have had distinct genetic origin. Records indicate that each of these resulted from the planting of seed from chance seed balls, but because of their similarity they are now grown mostly under the name Rural. The classification of American varieties by Stuart (1918) and the development of the certified seed-potato program did much to eliminate synonyms and meaningless variety names.

Methods of Origin

Potato varieties have originated by four distinct methods. In the order of numbers of existing commercial varieties these are (1) artificial or controlled hybridization, (2) mutation, (3) selection of seedlings from naturally produced seed balls, and (4) clonal selec-

tion. Until 1934 when Katahdin was introduced, the majority of
varieties represented production from chance seed balls. Well
known among such varieties were Garnet Chili, Early Rose, Early
Ohio, Burbank, Rural New Yorker No. 2, Carman No. 1, Carman
No. 3, Sir Walter Raleigh, and probably Irish Cobbler.

The difficulty of finding sufficient viable pollen delayed origin
through artificial hybridization; Bliss Triumph and Green Mountain were among the few important ones developed by this means.
Beginning with Katahdin in 1934, many new and valuable varieties
have been bred artificially as the technique of cross-pollination was
perfected and good pollen parents became available. In fact, the
variety Katahdin, because it produces viable pollen so plentifully,
has served as the male parent of many of our best present-day varieties. Among the varieties produced by hybridization are Chippewa,
Houma, Sebago, Mohawk, Pontiac, Sequoia, Teton, Erie, Ontario,
Warba, and Katahdin.

Fewer varieties originated by mutation because such varieties
occur accidentally in nature and are usually discovered only as some
physical character of the tuber exhibits a change of skin color or
texture. Among those originating by mutation are such well-known
varieties as Russet Burbank or Netted Gem, Russet Rural, Red
McClure, Pearl, Red Warba, Russet Sebago, and Pioneer Rural.
These varieties were discovered readily because each represented
a change from white to red or red to white color, or a change from
smooth to netted or netted to smooth skin. These sudden changes or
mutations occur commonly and are not difficult to find if one is ob-
serving.

Mutations are mainly of two types, namely, periclinal and sectorial chimeras. When the mutation involves a change of the entire
surface of the tuber it is called a periclinal chimera. When it takes
the form of a change in a section or portion of the tuber it represents
a sectorial chimera. In the latter case, one can develop a new variety
by merely cutting out the mutated area and planting it separately.
In this way Pearl can be obtained from Peoples, Red Warba from
Warba, or Russet Sebago from Sebago. Examples of origin from
periclinal chimeras may be represented by Russet Rural, Pioneer
Rural, Red Pontiac, and Red McClure (see figures 34 and 35).

Origin by clonal selection is discussed in a later chapter. To the
extent that such origin does not represent some heritably distinct

character, the product scarcely deserves to be called a new variety. Nevertheless many so-called varieties have been so originated, and among them are such important varieties as Number 9 and Heavy-weight. Both of these are supposedly clonal selections for high yield from existing varieties of the Rural type.

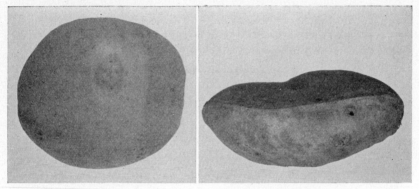

Fig. 34. Sectorial chimera in variety Peoples.

Fig. 35. Longitudinal sectorial chimera in Sebago.

History, Permanence, and the Theory of Senility

A number of factors encourage the development and introduction of new varieties. Chief among them is the demand from growers for varieties that have better "eye appeal" or market quality, greater disease resistance, earlier maturity, or better culinary quality. Yield is important but it is apparently less so than those tuber characters that attract the buyer in the retail market.

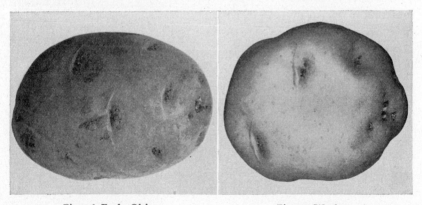

Fig. 36. Early Ohio.

Fig. 37. Warba.

In the early history of the United States, the principal varieties grown were introductions from Europe; the tubers were elongated, colored, and sometimes of colored flesh, poorly shaped, and deep-eyed. Among them were Cowhorn, Blue Mercer, Black Chenango, Garnet Chili, and Lady Finger. Severe damage from the late blight disease, *Phytophthora infestans,* about the middle of the nineteenth century, stimulated the search for disease-resistant varieties. Although many were introduced, few gave any relief. Thus the demand for new and better varieties continued. Some of the old varieties still exist, perhaps because of their tolerance to disease, heat, and drought. Most of them disappeared from commercial production after being in cultivation about 50 years. This gave rise to the theory of senility, which assumes that after about a half-century in asexual or vegetative propagation, all varieties become somehow devitalized and disappear because of age. Some authors have stated that to rejuvenate an old variety, it must again be grown from true seed. Neither of these theories can be substantiated by present-day evidence. Some of the oldest-known varieties are still in existence and apparently as vigorous as ever. Growing a variety from seed does not necessarily reinvigorate it, because in known instances the first generation from seed has shown a high percentage of virus-infected plants. If a variety is highly susceptible to disease or to unfavorable environment, it is likely to disappear from cultivation because of the difficulty of maintaining good seed. If it has characters of tuber that are unpopular, it is also likely to disappear and be replaced by more popular types.

Most investigators have discarded the theory of senility. Among these Krantz (1923) assembled several lots of Early Ohio variety from different sources in Minnesota and found that they exhibited distinct differences in tuber characters. When grown side by side in a particular environment, they tended to assume the same character, thus illustrating the influence of environment. He concluded that "varieties do not run into definite strains, that they are relatively stable under vegetative propagation, and that the method of asexual selection does not offer reasonable hope for their further improvement." More recently, Bushnell (1928) cited several instances in Ohio where very old varieties, among them Long John, in cultivation for over 90 years, have been maintained in high vigor either through tolerance of or resistance to disease and through

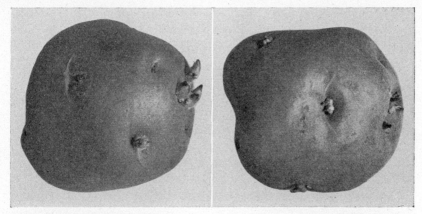

Fig. 38. Bliss Triumph.   *Fig. 39.* Irish Cobbler.

Fig. 40. Chippewa.   *Fig. 41.* White Rose.

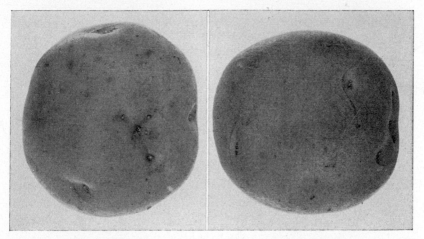

Fig. 42. Houma.   *Fig. 43.* Katahdin.

special measures to provide favorable environment. In contrast, it is well known that seed stocks, especially those of varieties susceptible to virus diseases, are very likely to degenerate in a comparatively short period of time.

Classification and Description

The grouping of varieties is a useful means of comparing them and eliminating synonyms insofar as the varieties have identical or

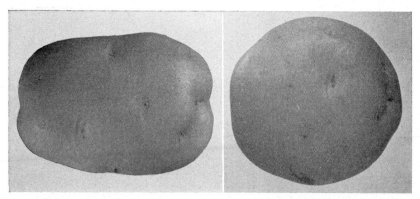

Fig. 44. Green Mountain.   Fig. 45. Kennebec.

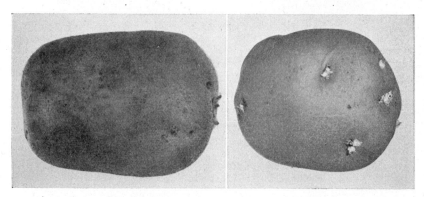

Fig. 46. Mohawk.   Fig. 47. Teton.

very similar characters. During the 50-year period 1860 to 1910, the number of named varieties became so large that the nomenclature reached a confused and somewhat meaningless state. By growing, storing, and studying all of the commercial varieties then grown in the United States, Stuart (1918) classified them into twelve groups, mainly on the basis of similarity of tuber characters. Each group was named for the most important variety in it, and all similar or identical varieties, including synonyms, were placed in it. This classification and the program of seed certification developed since then have done much to clarify variety nomenclature and to eliminate variety names. Since Stuart's classification, such groups as Early Michigan, Hebron, Peerless, and Uptodate have so declined in production that they no longer merit listing. Three other groups —Rose, Early Ohio, and Peachblow—are of only minor importance. The demand for varieties with greater disease resistance and better market quality resulted in a nationwide breeding program headed by the United States Department of Agriculture and supported by several co-operating state experiment stations. As the result of this effort, more than thirty new varieties have been named and introduced beginning with Katahdin in 1934. These varieties differ so widely in tuber characters, season of maturity, disease resistance, and quality factors that it hardly seems feasible to classify them into groups. Recognizing this fact, Clark and Lombard (1946) recently published descriptions of and a key to American potato varieties. Their list includes thirty-nine varieties, some of which are of only minor importance. Others introduced since are, of course, not included. Their key is based on flower color, tuber color, stem character, character of calyx, and tuber shape; it is of special value where variety identification is difficult. These authors, like Stuart, devoted much study to character and color of tuber sprouts as developed in diffused light and in darkness. Color plates of both blossoms and sprouts furnish a valuable reference to these varietal characters.

The grower and the student of varieties will find here a listing of those characters that may be of most use in choosing a variety and in distinguishing one variety from another, general descriptions of the varieties, and illustrations of the tubers of those varieties now of greatest commercial importance. A few varieties that are of recent origin but not yet very widely grown are purposely omitted. The descriptions that follow are of course subject to criticism in respect to accuracy and completeness. They were compiled from personal study of both plant and tuber material and from free use of published official descriptions, especially those of Folsom (1945), Clark and Lombard (1946), and Stevenson (1947).

TABLE 44. DESCRIPTION OF PLANTS OF TWENTY-SIX POTATO VARIETIES.

Variety	Growth Habit	Foliage Color	Leaf Character	Leaflet Size	Leaflet Texture	Blossom Color	Blossom Number
Burbank	Upright	Light	Open	Medium	Medium	White	Sparse
Chippewa	Spreading	Medium	Medium	Large	Smooth	Lavender	Medium
Cobbler	Upright	Dark	Medium	Medium	Medium	Lavender	Medium
Early Ohio	Upright	Light	Open	Medium	Medium	White	Sparse
Erie	Medium	Light	Medium	Medium	Smooth	White	Medium
Green Mountain	Upright	Medium	Medium	Medium	Smooth	White	Profuse
Houma	Spreading	Medium	Medium	Medium	Medium	White	Profuse
Jersey Redskin	Medium	Dark	Compact	Small	Rugose	Lavender	Medium
Katahdin	Spreading	Medium	Medium	Large	Medium	Lavender	Profuse
Kennebec	Medium	Medium	Medium	Large	Medium	White	Sparse
Mohawk	Upright	Medium	Medium	Medium	Smooth	Pale lavender	Medium
Norkota	Medium	Medium	Medium	Large	Smooth	White	Sparse
Ontario	Upright	Medium	Medium	Medium	Medium	Pale lavender	Sparse
Pawnee	Medium	Dark	Medium	Small	Medium	Purple	Sparse
Pontiac	Upright	Dark	Compact	Medium	Rugose	Lavender	Sparse
Red McClure	Medium	Medium	Medium	Medium	Medium	Lavender	Sparse
Red Warba	Spreading	Dark	Compact	Medium	Rugose	Lavender	Sparse
Rural	Upright	Dark	Medium	Small	Medium	Purple	Medium
Russet Burbank	Upright	Light	Open	Medium	Medium	White	Sparse
Russet Rural	Upright	Dark	Medium	Small	Medium	Purple	Medium
Sebago	Upright	Medium	Medium	Medium	Medium	Lavender	Profuse
Sequoia	Upright	Medium	Medium	Medium	Medium	Lavender	Medium
Teton	Spreading	Medium	Medium	Medium	Medium	White	Medium
Triumph	Spreading	Dark	Compact	Medium	Medium	White	Medium
Warba	Spreading	Dark	Compact	Medium	Rugose	Lavender	Sparse
White Rose	Spreading	Light	Open	Medium	Smooth	White	Sparse

TABLE 45. DESCRIPTION OF TUBERS OF TWENTY-SIX POTATO VARIETIES.

Variety	Skin Color	Skin Texture	Shape	Eye Number	Eye Depth	Color of Sprout Tips
Burbank	White	Smooth	Elliptical flattened	Many	Shallow	Pink
Chippewa	White	Smooth	Oblong flattened	Few	Shallow	Pink
Cobbler	White	Smooth	Cubical	Many	Deep	Pink
Early Ohio	Flesh	Smooth	Oval rounded	Many	Shallow	Pink
Erie	White	Smooth	Oval flattened	Medium	Medium	Pink
Green Mountain	Creamy white	Patchy netted	Oblong flattened	Many	Medium	White
Houma	White	Smooth	Short oblong rounded	Few	Shallow	Pink
Jersey Redskin	Red	Smooth	Elliptical flattened	Many	Shallow	Magenta
Katahdin	White	Smooth	Oblong rounded	Few	Shallow	Pink
Kennebec	White	Smooth	Oblong rounded	Medium	Medium	Pink
Mohawk	White	Flaky	Oblong flattened	Few	Shallow	Pink
Norkota	White	Flaky	Oval flattened	Medium	Medium	White
Ontario	White	Smooth	Oblong flattened	Medium	Shallow	White
Pawnee	White	Smooth	Oval flattened	Few	Shallow	Purple
Pontiac	Dark red	Smooth	Oval rounded	Many	Medium	Magenta
Red McClure	Pink	Coarsely netted	Oval rounded	Medium	Shallow	Magenta
Red Warba	Red	Smooth	Cubical	Many	Medium	Magenta
Rural	White	Smooth	Oval flattened	Few	Shallow	Purple
Russet Burbank	Light russet	Netted	Elliptical flattened	Many	Shallow	Pink
Russet Rural	Dark russet	Netted	Oval flattened	Few	Shallow	Purple
Sebago	White	Smooth	Oval rounded	Medium	Shallow	Pink
Sequoia	White	Smooth	Oval flattened	Few	Shallow	White
Teton	White	Smooth	Oblong flattened	Few	Shallow	White
Triumph	Dark pink	Smooth	Cubical	Many	Medium	Magenta
Warba	White (pink eye)	Smooth	Cubical	Many	Deep	Pink
White Rose	White	Smooth	Elliptical flattened	Many	Shallow	Magenta

TABLE 46. PERFORMANCE CHARACTERS OF TWENTY-SIX POTATO VARIETIES.

Variety	Maturity	Resistant to	Soil Adaptation	Storage Quality	Starch Content
Burbank	Midseason		Narrow	Fair	Very high
Chippewa	Medium early	Mild mosaic	Wide	Poor	Low
Cobbler	Early		Narrow	Good	Medium to high
Early Ohio	Very early		Narrow	Fair	Medium
Erie	Late	Ring rot and mosaic	Wide	Good	Medium
Green Mountain	Late		Narrow	Good	Very high
Houma	Midseason	Mosaic and leaf roll	Narrow	Fair	High
Jersey Redskin	Very late		Wide	Good	Medium to high
Katahdin	Midseason	Leaf roll and mosaic	Wide	Good	Medium to low
Kennebec	Late	Late blight	Wide	Good	High
Mohawk	Late	Mild mosaic	Narrow	Good	Very high
Norkota	Late	Hopperburn	Wide	Good	Medium
Ontario	Very late	Scab	Wide	Good	Medium
Pawnee	Midseason		Wide	Good	Medium to high
Pontiac	Late		Wide	Good	Low
Red McClure	Midseason		Narrow	Good	Medium to high
Red Warba	Very early		Narrow	Fair	Medium to low
Rural	Late		Wide	Good	High
Russet Burbank	Midseason		Narrow	Fair	Very high
Russet Rural	Late	Scab	Wide	Good	High
Sebago	Late	Scab and blight	Wide	Poor	Medium
Sequoia	Very late	Mosaic and leaf roll	Wide	Good	Medium
Teton	Midseason to late	Ring rot and X virus	Wide	Fair	Medium
Triumph	Very early		Narrow	Fair	Medium to low
Warba	Very early		Narrow	Fair	Medium to low
White Rose	Midseason		Narrow	Good	Low

Disease-resistant Varieties

There always has been a demand for blight-resistant and scab-resistant varieties. Such varieties are now available, but, until their adaptability to the demands of growers and handlers has been fur-

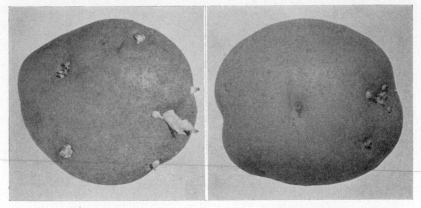

Fig. 48. Erie.   Fig. 49. Rural.

Fig. 50. Russet Rural.   Fig. 51. Pontiac.

ther established, it is not known to what extent they will become important. Reddick and Peterson (1947) officially described five varieties that are highly resistant to late blight, *Phytophthora infestans*. These are Ashworth, Chenango, Empire, Placid, and Virgil. All of these produce white tubers of acceptable appearance and quality. Chenango is medium early, Ashworth, Placid, and Virgil are mid-

season, and Empire is very late in maturity. Other blight resistant
varieties developed by the same breeders but which have not yet
been officially described are Cortland, Essex, Fillmore, Glenmeer,
Harford, Madison, and Snowdrift. These varieties derived their
blight resistance from *Solanum demissum,* a species obtained from
Mexico by Reddick.

Fig. 52. Sebago.   *Fig. 53.* Burbank.

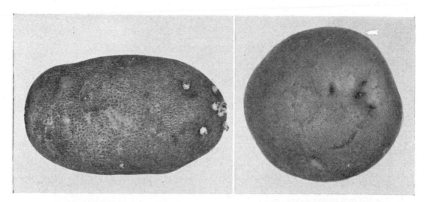

Fig. 54. Russet Burbank.   *Fig. 55.* Red McClure.

After years of effort to develop varieties resistant to common
scab, *Actinomyces scabies,* only three of those developed are of much
importance commercially. These are Menominee, Ontario and
Russet Sebago. Menominee was developed at the Michigan Experiment Station and proved to be both resistant and high-yielding.
Like many other scab-resistant seedlings it has a rough shape and
flaky skin. Blodgett and Stevenson (1946) officially described three
scab-resistant varieties named Ontario, Seneca, and Cayuga. Of
these, Ontario is superior in resistance, yield, and marketability.

It can be grown on extremely scabby soil and, unlike most other scab-resistant varieties, its tuber is of smooth skin, excellent shape, and fair culinary quality. Cayuga and Seneca are of midseason maturity but not equal to Ontario in yield or marketability.

New Varieties

Every year a few new varieties appear for trial. Some of these soon disappear, others find limited adaptation, and still others remain for longer trial. Such varieties, together with the state or agency responsible for their introduction, are as follows: Calrose (California), Chisago (Minnesota), De Soto (Louisiana), Earlaine (U.S. Department of Agriculture), Earlaine No. 2 (Maine), Golden (U.S. Department of Agriculture), Kasota (Nebraska-Minnesota), La Salle (Louisiana), Marygold (Maryland), Mesaba (Minnesota), Pennigan (Pennsylvania), Pocono (Pennsylvania), and Potomac (Maryland).

Older Commercial Varieties

As new and improved varieties are introduced, some of the older ones very naturally are superseded and gradually disappear. Notable among those still grown but rapidly declining in production are Blue Victor, Brown Beauty, Early Rose, Idaho Rural, Spalding Rose No. 4, and Uptodate. (For a description of these refer to Clark and Lombard [1946].)

Synonyms

Several of the commercial varieties described and illustrated in this chapter are grown under other names which should be considered synonyms. In the case of Green Mountain, Red McClure, Rural, and Uptodate, the names listed as synonyms may represent varieties of distinct origin. Because of their similarity to the standard variety, however, it seems practical to list them as synonyms:

Variety	Synonyms
Green Mountain	Carman No. 1, Delaware, Gold Coin, State of Maine, White Gold
Jersey Redskin	Dakota Red, Evergreen, Late Rose
Red McClure	Perfect Peachblow

Variety	*Synonyms*
Rural	Carman No. 3, Heavyweight, Knoxall, No. 9, Rural New Yorker No. 2, Sir Walter Raleigh
Russet Burbank	Idaho Russet, Netted Gem
Russet Rural	Dibble's Russet, Golden Petoskey
Triumph	Red Bliss, Stray Beauty
Uptodate	Charles Downing, Idaho Rural
White Rose	American Giant, Jersey Giant, Wisconsin Pride

Regional Importance

Among the factors that determine the commercial importance of a variety in a region are its adaptation to climate and soil and its ability to satisfy the seasonal demands of the market for which it is grown. Whereas the southern states once grew only early-maturing varieties for northern markets, they now also grow several

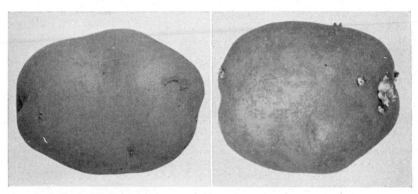

Fig. 56. British Queen.   *Fig. 57.* Ontario.

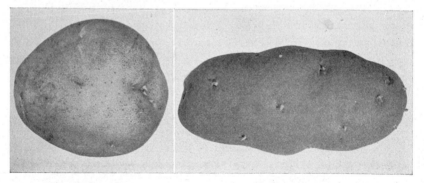

Fig. 58. Sequoia.   *Fig. 59.* Late Rose.

late-maturing varieties which develop good tuber size long before maturity. For example, Katahdin, Sebago, and Pontiac are now grown in the far South where formerly only Triumph, Cobbler, and Spalding Rose were grown. Pontiac, a late-maturing, red-skinned variety, is now marketed in northern markets by southern growers, and by Nebraska growers who formerly grew the early-maturing, red-skinned Triumph. Early Ohio has been largely superseded in the Red River Valley of North Dakota and Minnesota by Cobbler because the latter yields much better. Such varieties as Katahdin, Sebago, Rural, and Pontiac are adapted to a wide range of soil and climate. In contrast, Green Mountain, Houma, Russet Burbank, Cobbler, Mohawk, and White Rose are susceptible to most diseases and to heat and drought, and they should be grown only where the soil is loamy, the climate cool, and the grower equipped to spray or dust thoroughly against blight. The regions where the principal varieties are most extensively grown are given below:

Variety	Region
Burbank	California, Oregon, Washington
Chippewa	New England, middle Atlantic states, upper Mississippi Valley, Atlantic seaboard states
Early Ohio	Red River Valley in Minnesota and North Dakota
Green Mountain	New England, New York
Houma	New England, New York
Jersey Redskin	New Jersey, North Carolina
Katahdin	New England, middle Atlantic and Atlantic seaboard states, Ohio
Mohawk	Maine, New York
Ontario	New York
Pawnee	Colorado, Nebraska
Pontiac	Michigan, Nebraska, New York, Gulf states
Red McClure	Colorado
Red Warba	Minnesota, North Dakota
Rural	New York, Wisconsin
Russet Burbank	Idaho, California, Oregon, Utah, Washington
Russet Rural	Michigan, Pennsylvania, New York
Sebago	New England, middle Atlantic states, Alabama, Florida, Atlantic seaboard states

Variety	Region
Sequoia	North Carolina, New York
Teton	Wyoming, New York
Triumph	Gulf states, Colorado, Nebraska, lower Mississippi Valley, Texas, Wyoming, South Dakota
Warba	Minnesota, Missouri, North Dakota
White Rose	California, Oregon, Washington, North Dakota

The importance of a given variety in any given region may be expected to change as the experience of growers with new varieties indicates their superiority.

Variety Testing

The introduction of many new varieties in recent years has stimulated interest in variety testing. The objective is to compare the new varieties with standard varieties in yield, season of maturity, habit of growth, disease and insect resistance, regional adaptation,

Fig. 60. Studying new varieties in a variety field trial.

marketability, culinary quality, and storability. To accomplish these objectives, the test plot should be so designed that the results can be analyzed statistically and varieties of similar habits of growth and maturity can be readily compared. The soil should be uniform and planting and cultural care as nearly identical as possible. It is also important that the seed stocks be free from virus disease and be so stored and handled that they are in a similar condition of sprout growth. Single row plots of each variety should be replicated at least four times, the rows preferably 25 to 50 feet long. It is also well to group the varieties according to season of maturity so that early can be compared with early, late with late, and very late with very late. In each replication the varieties should be completely randomized to reduce the effect of competition for space to a minimum. Another factor to consider is the effect of tractor and sprayer-wheel injury on yield. Vine lifters do not completely eliminate this effect because some damage is done as the tractor and sprayer wheels compact the soil and injure the potato plant roots.

Hardenburg (1948) studied the effect of sprayer-wheel injury in a test of twenty-four varieties planted in randomized blocks. Those replicates contacted on one side yielded an average of 22 per cent less than the uninjured replicates of the same variety. In interpreting results of variety tests, too much importance is often put on small differences in yield. Statistical analyses of the significance of differences found in well-planned variety yield tests have usually shown that differences of 30 to 75 bushels to the acre are necessary for significance with odds of 19 to 1. At best, the results are usually applicable only to the area in which the test is made and for the seasonal and soil conditions involved.

Choosing a Variety for Production

In selecting a variety for production in a particular region, several considerations are of basic importance. The variety should be adapted to the soil and climate of the locality. Some varieties are more sensitive to environment than are others. Popularity in the local market or for out-of-season markets at long distance may greatly influence demand and selling price. Red McClures grown in the San Luis Valley of Colorado usually bring high prices in the Chicago market in season. One should not grow such blight-susceptible varieties as Green Mountain, Mohawk, and Houma unless he is well-equipped for thorough spraying or dusting with the appropriate fungicide. Sebago and Chippewa sprout early and are notably poor keepers, hence they should be marketed early or stored in a well-controlled low-temperature storage. Ontario, because of its high resistance to scab, is a good choice to grow on a scab-infested soil. For the home garden where early maturity and disease resistance are usually important, Cobbler, Warba, Chippewa, Katahdin, and Sebago are recommended.

No single variety has yet been developed that possesses all of the characters desired. High yield is important, but it is by no means the only reason for popularity of a variety. Marketability or eye appeal and reliability as to crop are of prime importance. For these reasons, mainly, Katahdin has become the most widely grown variety in America. In total yield and in starch content, it seldom ranks as high as Green Mountain, Russet Burbank, and Sebago. Its great popularity, however, is due to its marketability and the fact that, no matter how late it is planted or how unfavorable the growth conditions are, it usually produces a fair crop of marketable tubers.

To be popular, a variety should be at least fairly resistant to blight, scab, virus diseases, and insects and should be tolerant of heat and drought. A variety with high starch content, resulting in whiteness of flesh and mealiness, is usually preferred for baking, but varieties possessing this character are usually most difficult to grow. Varieties differ also in their tendency to blacken after cooking and to produce second-growth and hollow-heart tubers. Such defects are very common to varieties of the Rural type. Russet Burbank is highly susceptible to knobby tubers, and one of the principal faults of Sequoia is oversize and hollow heart.

REFERENCES

Blodgett, F. M., and F. J. Stevenson. The new scab-resistant potatoes, Ontario, Seneca, and Cayuga. Amer. Potato Jour. 23, No. 9, 1946.

Bushnell, John. Do potato varieties degenerate in warm climates? Jour. Heredity 19, No. 3, 1928.

Clark, C. F. and P. M. Lombard. Descriptions of and key to American potato varieties. U.S. Dept. Agr. Circ. 741, 1946.

Folsom, Donald. Potato varieties: the newly named, the commercial, and some that are useful in breeding. Amer. Potato Jour. 22, No. 8, 1945.

Hardenburg, E. V. Effect of sprayer-wheel injury on the yield of potatoes. Amer. Potato Jour. 25, No. 4, 1948.

Krantz, Fred A. Permanence of variety in the potato. Jour. Agr. Research 23, No. 12, 1923.

Reddick, Donald, and L. C. Peterson. New blight-resistant varieties. Amer. Potato Jour. 24, No. 10, 1947.

Stevenson, F. J. New varieties of potatoes. Amer. Potato Jour. 24, No. 8, 1947.

Stuart, William. Group classification and varietal descriptions of some American potatoes. U.S. Dept. Agr. Bul. 176, 1918.

CHAPTER 9

Diseases and Disease Control

IT DOES NOT SEEM feasible to attempt to evaluate the reduction in yield or the economic loss of the potato crop in the United States caused annually by diseases. The loss is considerable, and millions of dollars are spent on equipment, labor, and materials to reduce it.

Not all diseases of potatoes are troublesome in any one region but certain ones are more or less prevalent wherever the crop is grown. Weather and soil conditions, intensity of production, rotation practices, and the prevalence of insect vectors vary in different areas and in different seasons, and they largely determine the importance and methods of control. No grower can afford not to observe the disease-control program recommended for his particular locality. The amount of money justified for disease control depends on the acreage grown, the importance of the disease involved, and whether other factors that affect yield are favorable. For example, it is not economical to invest much in disease control if soil conditions are poor, the stand of plants is sparse, and the quality of seed is inferior.

Seed-borne Diseases

Every potato grower is confronted with the question whether his present stock of seed potatoes is healthy enough to justify planting it. The decision should be based on whether the amount of disease present will reduce the yield enough to justify the cost of new seed containing less disease. Seed-borne diseases are numerous; they include both the surface types, such as rhizoctonia and scab, and the internally borne types, such as mosaic, leaf roll and spindle tuber. The latter diseases are difficult, usually impossible, to control by simply selecting good-looking tubers. That is the principal reason why buying certified seed is a fairly sure means of procuring seed that carries a minimum of virus diseases.

Pathologists have determined that a plant affected with leaf roll yields about one-third as much as a healthy plant; mosaic reduces the yield somewhat less. Whenever the population of leaf-roll plants in a field exceeds 10 per cent, it is profitable to discard the crop and purchase certified seed or seed known to be healthy. The following example illustrates how to decide when such a change of seed would be economically desirable. The premium cost of certified seed is usually not over 40 to 50 cents the bushel above the market value of table potatoes. Assuming a field shows 20-per-cent leaf roll and yields 200 bushels to the acre, the potential crop might well be 230 bushels if the seed were healthy. The 30 bushels lost because of leaf roll, at $1.50 a bushel, would represent a loss of $45.00. Replacing the seed with 25 bushels of certified stock costing a premium of $0.40 a bushel would cost $10.00. In this case the gain from using certified seed would be $35.00.

The first certified seed was grown in Wisconsin in 1914 and in New York in 1915. The demand came from growers in Long Island, New Jersey, and farther south. At that time, seed stocks were badly infected with virus diseases. Careful inspection by trained inspectors made it possible to certify that certain fields showed less than the maximum tolerance of disease prescribed in seed standards set by state agencies. In 1947, over 44 million bushels of seed were grown and certified in the United States, most of them in Maine, Minnesota, North Dakota, Michigan, New York, and other northern states. To succeed as a grower of certified seed potatoes, it is necessary to plant healthy seed, to rogue diseased plants, to spray or dust thoroughly to control insect vectors, and to store, grade, and pack to meet the demands of the seed buyer. Seed production practices and the usual techniques of seed improvement and certification have been well reviewed by Dykstra (1948).

Classification of Diseases

Every potato grower should be familiar with the symptoms of the principal diseases common to his locality. Unless he can identify them by name he is certainly not in a position to know and apply the appropriate control measures. He can usually acquire much useful information from neighbors and from publicly supported extension agencies without cost. It is especially important that the grower be familiar with such prevalent and serious diseases as late blight, *Phytophthora infestans,* bacterial ring rot, *Corynebacterium sepedonicum,* mosaic, and leaf roll. They occur widely and may cause severe losses unless adequate control measures are applied. All potato diseases can be classified according to cause or causal organism as bacterial, fungous, virus, slime mold, insect, physiological, nematode, or nonparasitic. This type of classification is useful in defining methods of overwintering and control but much less so in describing the disease. The key to diseases presented by

Fig. 61. Old potato refuse piles furnish a source of infection of the late blight disease.

Dykstra (1948) is based on whether the disease affects plant or tuber; in addition about twenty-five diseases are described according to their symptomology.

Among the diseases affecting both plant and tuber are late blight, bacterial ring rot, yellow dwarf, several species of wilt, blackleg, psyllid yellows, spindle tuber, rhizoctonia, and brown rot. Those affecting mainly the foliage are early blight, hopperburn, mosaic, leaf roll, and purple top. Others which are evident mainly on the tubers are blackheart, nematode, common scab, powdery scab, hollow heart, leak, net necrosis, silver scurf, spindling sprout, and wart.

The use of disease-resistant varieties when available is an effective way to reduce disease to a minimum. For most diseases, no one control measure is adequate. The following classification is indicative of the principal controls for the diseases listed:

Choice of seed:

bacterial ring rot	spindle tuber	wilts
leaf roll	spindling sprout	blackleg
mosaic	yellow dwarf	purple top

Crop rotation:

| common scab | rhizoctonia | wilts |
| powdery scab | wart | yellow dwarf |

Seed treatment (surface disinfestation):

| common scab | silver scurf | blackleg |
| rhizoctonia | bacterial ring rot | powdery scab |

Spraying or dusting:

| early blight | late blight | hopperburn |
| psyllid yellows | purple top | virus diseases |

Soil treatment (chemical):

| common scab | nematodes |

An alphabetical classification of the most important potato diseases is given in table 47.

Description and Control

Of the twenty-six diseases listed in table 47, thirteen are of enough importance to warrant a brief discussion of their symptomology and control.[1]

Bacterial ring rot, *Corynebacterium sepedonicum,* is an extremely infectious bacterial disease that occurs in nearly all potato states. There is no tolerance for it in certified seed. It causes the lower leaves to turn yellow, finally causing wilting and death of the entire plant. Squeezing a transection of either stem or tuber causes a yellowish white, cheesy exudate to emerge from the vascular ring. In advanced stages, the cortex separates from the medulla, and the center of the tuber becomes a soft slimy rot. The tuber may break down at the surface, starting usually at or near the eyes. The disease does not overwinter in the soil. Control is by the use of clean seed

---

[1] For source material, several references listed at the end of this chapter have been freely used.

Table 47. A CLASSIFICATION OF POTATO DISEASES.

Disease	Type	Portion of Plant Affected	Regions of Occurrence in U.S.	Method of Hibernation	Control Measures
Blackheart	Physiological	Tubers	General	None	Proper aeration in storage and shipping
Blackleg (*Erwinia phytophthora*)	Bacterial	Foliage and tubers	Northern states and Canada	In seed	Clean seed and disinfesting of cutting knife
Brown rot (*Bacterium solanacearum*)	Bacterial	Foliage and tubers	Gulf states and South Atlantic states	Weed hosts and in soil	Rotation and clean culture
Common scab (*Actinomyces scabies*)	Bacterial or fungous	Tubers	General	On seed and in soil	As for rhizoctonia, keep soil pH below 5.4
Early blight (*Alternaria solani*)	Fungous	Foliage mainly	General	In trash in field	Bordeaux mixture or other copper fungicides
Fusarium tuber rot (*Fusarium eumartii*)	Fungous	Tubers and foliage	General	In seed and soil	Clean seed and crop rotation
Fusarium wilt (*Fusarium oxysporum*)	Fungous	Foliage and tubers	General	In seed and soil	Clean seed and crop rotation
Hollow heart	Physiological	Tubers	General	None	Close planting
Hopperburn	Physiological	Leaf margins	General	None	DDT in spray to control leaf hoppers
Late blight (*Phytophthora infestans*)	Fungous	Foliage and tubers	Humid regions	In seed	Bordeaux mixture or other copper fungicides
Leaf roll	Virus	Foliage	General	In seed	Seed from clean fields and control of aphis
Leak (*Phthium debaryanum*)	Fungous	Tuber	Nebraska and Idaho	Not known	Avoid bruising and handle at low temperature
Mosaic	Virus	Foliage	General	In seed	As for leaf roll
Nematode (eel worm) (*Heterodera marioni*)	Root-knot	Tubers and roots	General	In soil, in seed, on equipment	Avoid host plants; grow grass or grain crops; summer fallow; soil fumigation
(*Heterodera rostochiensis*)	Golden	Roots	Nassau County, N.Y.		
(*Ditylenchus destructor*)	Potato rot	Tubers	Idaho		
(*Pratylenchus scribneri*)	Meadow	Tubers	General		

TABLE 47. A CLASSIFICATION OF POTATO DISEASES (*cont.*).

Disease	Type	Portion of Plant Affected	Regions of Occurrence in U.S.	Method of Hibernation	Control Measures
Net necrosis	Virus	Tubers	General	In seed	As for leaf roll
Powdery scab (*Spongospora subterranea*)	Slime mold	Tubers	Northern states and Canada	On seed and in soil	As for rhizoctonia
Psyllid yellows	Similar to virus	Foliage and tubers	Nebraska and Rocky Mt. States	Infested trash in field	Control of psyllid by sulfur dust or lime-sulfur spray
Purple top	Virus	Foliage	W. Va., Minn., N.Y., Pa., and Md.	Alternate plant hosts	Control of aster leaf hopper
Rhizoctonia (*Corticium vagum*)	Fungous	Tubers, new sprouts, and base of stems	General	On seed and in soil	Clean seed, crop rotation, and seed treatment
Ring rot (*Corynebacterium sepedonicum*)	Bacterial	Foliage and tubers	General	In seed, storage, and equipment	Clean seed, sterilization of storage, containers, and equipment
Silver scurf (*Spondylocladium atrovirens*)	Fungous	Tubers	General	On seed	Clean seed and crop rotation
Spindle tuber	Virus	Foliage and tubers	General	In seed	As for mosaic, also sterilize cutting knife
Spindling sprout	Nonparasitic	Sprout growth from tubers	General	Seed	Seed selection and good storage
Verticillium wilt (*Verticillium alboatrum*)	Fungous	Foliage and tubers	General	In seed and soil	Clean seed and crop rotation
Wart (*Synchitrium endobioticum*)	Slime mold	Tubers	Mining districts of Pa.	In seed and soil	Long crop rotation, quarantine, and immune varieties
Yellow dwarf	Virus	Foliage and tubers	Scattered areas in U.S.	In soil and seed	Clean seed and crop rotation

and disinfesting of storage walls, containers, and implements. Spread of the disease when cutting seed should be avoided by disinfesting the knife.

Blackleg, *Erwinia phytophthora,* is a bacterial disease most damaging in the cooler areas of the northern states. It causes a yellowing of the lower leaves and its most prominent symptom is the black soft decay at the base of the stem. In advanced stages the bacterial soft rot may enter the stem end of the tuber and destroy most of the medullary area. The organism overwinters in the seed and in the soil. Control is through using clean seed and seed treatment to prevent spread at time of cutting seed. Seed-corn maggot may carry the organism from soil to seed pieces causing them to rot.

Fig. 62. Potato crop a total loss from late blight disease.

Common scab, *Actinomyces scabies,* causes rough irregular lesions on the tuber surface and may disfigure potatoes enough to disqualify them for No. 1 grade. Blodgett and Howe (1934) sampled 313 fields in New York, and they showed the relation of soil pH to the incidence of scab on the tubers. They found least scab where the soil pH was 4.3 to 5.4, more where it was 7.5 to 8.5 and most where it was 5.45 to 7.4. Millipedes and maggots of the scab gnat feed in scab spots causing pitted scab and accentuating the damage. Scab is worse in dry than in wet seasons. Control is by regulating soil reaction, using sulfur with the fertilizer, seed treatment, rotation, and the use of scab-resistant varieties such as **Ontario**, **Menominee**, and **Sebago**.

Early blight, *Alternaria solani,* is widely distributed but generally most severe in the warmer, drier areas. It affects the foilage by causing small, rounded dead spots with target-board markings, but these are not usually serious except in extreme cases. Small, dried lesions sometimes occur on the surface of the tuber, the damage being due largely to disfiguration. Control is by spraying with Bordeaux mixture, Fermate, Zerlate, or one of the organic fungicides.

Fusarium spp., *F. oxysporum* and *F. eumartii,* are rather common forms of wilt; so called because they result in a plugging of the sap tubes or xylem vessels and subsequent wilting and dying of the foliage. *F. oxysporum* or common wilt causes a dying of the lower leaves first and a necrosis of the vascular ring at the stem end of the tuber. The disease is worse in a dry season and a dry soil than otherwise. *F. eumartii* differs from the more common form in that the upper leaves die first, and the necrotic areas in the tuber are not confined to the vascular ring but often appear as reddish brown flecks of dead tissue throughout the flesh. Both forms of wilt are difficult to control. Planting diseased seed does not necessarily reproduce the disease—it may depend on seasonal weather and soil conditions. Control is by using clean seed, rotation, irrigation, and seed treatment.

Late blight, *Phytophthora infestans,* has without question, always been the most serious of all potato diseases in the United States. It was directly responsible for the Irish famine in 1846, and since then it has caused serious losses, especially in the humid regions where rainfall was above normal in the northeastern states. Late blight spores develop as a mold on the underside of potato leaflets when the air is moist, the plants are wet, and the air temperature is below 50° F. Under such conditions the spores germinate and infect the upper surface of the leaves unless the latter are protected by a fungicide. Tubers are infected as the spores fall from the leaves and are washed through the soil to make contact. Infection is more rapid and more severe in heavy than in the better-aerated soils. A dry reddish-brown rot through the cortical layer and irregular sunken areas of skin are characteristic of badly infected tubers (see figure 63). This decay may be followed by saprophytic organisms causing soft rot in moist storage. The late blight organism is not a sapro-phyte and so does not spread after the foliage is dead. The influence of maturity on spread was reported by Mills (1938). He inoculated plants of different physiological age using short-day, day-length neutral, and long-day varieties in the greenhouse and found no influence of age of plant or of photoperiod on susceptibility to late blight. The disease overwinters mainly in infected tubers which,

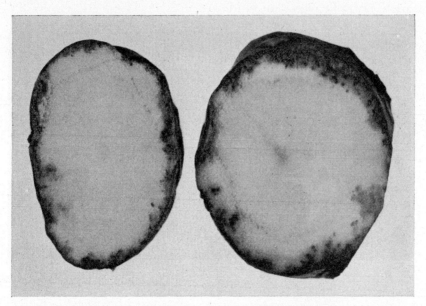

Fig. 63. Cross section of tuber showing late blight dry rot. (Plant Pathology Dept., Cornell Univ.)

when planted, send up sprouts on which the new spores develop. Also, spores may be carried on moisture-laden air, from volunteer plants and from old potato refuse piles, to near-by fields of potatoes. Control is mainly by thorough spraying or dusting, by sanitary cultural practices, clean seed, and the use of blight-resistant varie-ties. Further discussion of other factors influencing the spread of late blight appears in the chapter on harvesting.

Leaf roll is probably the most serious of the virus diseases be-cause of its widespread occurrence, its effect on yield and the diffi-culty of its control. Katahdin and Houma are among the few varieties resistant to and tolerant of leaf roll. The disease causes an upward rolling of the leaflets first appearing at the bottom of

5222

the plant. These leaflets are usually brittle, and thick from the accumulation of carbohydrates, and in advanced stages they give the plant an upright, staring habit. Current-season infection of certain varieties produces net necrosis in the flesh of the tuber. This netting is worst at the stem end and may make the tubers worthless for market. Control is mainly by clean seed, thorough roguing of the seed plot, early harvesting, and spraying to control the aphids which are likely to be prevalent in the fall.

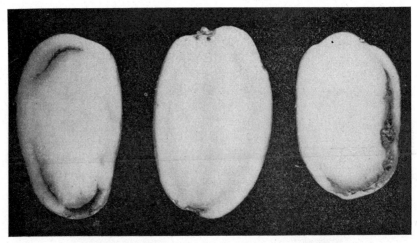

Fig. 64. Cross section of tuber infected with bacterial ring rot.

Mosaic is second only to leaf roll as a virus disease of potatoes. It has two principal types, mild and rugose; they differ mainly in severity, the mild form causing a mottling of the leaflets and a slight reduction in yield, the rugose form causing the leaves and stems to become brittle and to die. The mottling caused by mild mosaic is most easily observed early in the season and on cool, cloudy days. Mosaic does not produce symptoms in the tuber. Control is mainly by the use of seed from healthy plants, by thorough roguing of the seed plot, and by control of the potato aphis, which acts as the principal vector. Katahdin, Chippewa, Houma, and Sebago are practically immune to mild mosaic. Many varieties appear to be susceptible to the rugose form.

Nematode or eel worm causes serious losses in certain areas. Of the several forms found in America, the four which do most damage to potatoes are listed in table 47. Damage involves not only reduction in yield but also the appearance of the tubers except in case of the Golden Nematode. The latter attaches to the roots in the form of cysts, saps the vitality of the plant, reduces yield, but does not materially injure the tubers. Control is difficult because the organism lives over in the soil as cysts that contain and protect the eggs. In this way the population builds up until it is no longer profitable to grow potatoes or other host crops on the infested field. Control is by the use of strong soil fumigants and by not growing potatoes more often than once in 6 or 8 years.

Fig. 65. Servicing a 10-row, trailer type potato sprayer. Note equipment with brush type of boom.

Psyllid yellows is a systemic disease of some importance in Nebraska and the Rocky Mountain states. Although not a virus disease, it behaves much the same. The leaves become yellow and later reddish; eventually the plant may die. The upper leaves roll upward first, the plant assumes a compact pyramidal shape, and the tubers remain small and often form a chain along the stolon. The disease is caused by a toxic substance injected by the potato psyllid *Paratrioza cockerelli*. Control is by spraying to control this insect. The disease is not carried over in the seed tuber, but infected tubers usually produce weak plants.

Rhizoctonia or black scurf is a very common disease caused by the fungus *Rhizoctonia solani*. The fungus is most commonly recognized in its resting stage when it appears on the surface of the tuber as coal-black bits of dried mycelium. In this way it overwinters on the seed tuber and, unless killed by previous treatment, it resumes growth when the seed is planted in moist soil; severe girdling of the tender new sprouts results. It is this injury that often accounts for slow, uneven stands of plants, especially when the seedbed is cold. Plant symptoms of rhizoctonia injury include aerial tubers, some rolling of the leaflets, and the development of pigmentation. The fungus also lives in the soil and is favored by the presence of decaying organic matter, stable manure, and frequent cropping to potatoes. Control is by rotation and seed treatment to disinfest the surface of the tuber. The presence of black sclerotial bodies on the

Fig. 66. Saddleback type of 10-row sprayer equipped with Nixon type of boom or drop nozzles. Two rubber-tired front tractor wheels reduce vine injury. (Burt Straw, Coudersport, Pa.)

seed tuber indicates the need for treatment, before cutting, with formaldehyde, or a mercury compound. Greensprouting of seed is also recommended as a means of adding resistance against sprout injury.

Spindle tuber is a virus disease carried in seed, deriving its name from its effect in making the tubers abnormally elongated or spindle-shaped, deep-eyed, and pointed at the stem end. The plant shows a spindly, upright habit and a characteristic twisting of the terminal leaflets. Spindle tuber is difficult to diagnose, especially early in the season, and although it is common to all varieties it is especially serious in Cobbler, Triumph, and Teton when grown in the Great Plains and Rocky Mountain areas. For control, clean seed, disinfesting of the cutting knife, and roguing diseased units in the tuber-unit seed plot are most effective.

Yellow dwarf is caused by a virus which is transmitted by the clover leaf hopper *Aceratagallia sanguinolenta.* The name derives from the fact that the disease yellows and dwarfs the plant severely and usually early in its development. The leaves become rugose and rolled downward. The tubers are badly malformed and usually show growth cracks and severe internal necrosis throughout the pith and internal phloem. In severe cases the yield is almost negligible, and the few tubers developed are worthless. Control consists in planting the field some distance from any meadow containing clover and in the use of clean seed. The Sebago variety is said to have considerable resistance to yellow dwarf.

Fungicides

Among the diseases which can be, in large part, controlled by spraying or dusting with fungicides are early blight, *Alternaria solani,* and late blight, *Phytophthora infestans.* Fortunately these diseases and most of the common foliage insects can be controlled simultaneously by including an insecticide with the fungicide in the spray or dust mixture.

Bordeaux mixture has been the principal fungicide used for the control of early and late blight for many years and still is considered superior to most of the new materials for this purpose. Bordeaux mixture consists of copper sulfate with hydrated lime and water, the chemicals forming a suspension which, when sprayed on the potato leaf, forms a film of protection against the entrance of blight spores as they germinate. The formula for Bordeaux mixture as a spray is commonly 5-5-50 or 10-10-100, the first figure representing copper sulfate, the second hydrated lime; the third water. In making Bordeaux mixture, it is advisable not to combine the copper sulfate and lime before one or the other is well diluted with water. The usual procedure is first to start filling the sprayer tank with water and to start the agitator. A weighed amount of powdered crystals or the snow form of copper sulfate is then placed in the funnel through which the water is being run into the sprayer. When the spray tank is about two-thirds full, an equivalent amount of high-grade hydrated lime is placed in the funnel and washed through a screen into the tank.

There is some evidence that the lime in Bordeaux not only tends to stunt plant growth but also attracts aphids. Better results are sometimes obtained when the formula consists of one-half as much lime as of copper sulfate. Bordeaux mixture is also applied as a dust the formula of which is usually 20-80, or 20 parts of monohydrated copper sulfate and 80 parts of hydrated lime. When calcium arsenate was the most popular insecticide and the mixture was 20-20-60, the insecticide, if needed, was substituted for a portion of the lime. Since DDT has become the almost universally used insecticide for potatoes, however, it must be applied either with the spray or with one of the fixed copper dusts, as it is not compatible with Bordeaux dust. Copper is the toxic ingredient in Bordeaux while the function of lime is to prevent burning by the copper and to form a suspension which adheres to the leaf very effectively. Wilson and Runnels

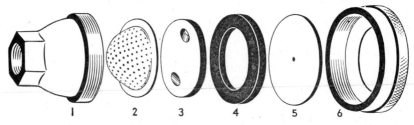

Fig. 67. Parts of a spray nozzle: (1) base, (2) strainer, (3) whirl disc, (4) rubber gasket, (5) spray disc, (6) cap. (After Rose, R. C., Minn. Extension Folder 76, 1939.)

(1935) in Ohio, by varying the ratio of the copper and the lime in Bordeaux, found that an increase in either caused an increase in transpiration, an increase in water requirement, and a decrease in growth of the plant. Therefore Bordeaux is definitely not a plant stimulant, and when its use has resulted in an increase in yield, that has been the result of its effectiveness in blight control.

Fungicidal sprays other than Bordeaux consist of Fermate, an iron compound, Zerlate, a zinc compound, and several organics such as Phygon and Dithane. Odland (1946), in a year when late blight was severe, compared thirteen materials with Bordeaux in randomized blocks. The Bordeaux-sprayed plots yielded 50 bushels per acre more than any of the other materials used. The actual percentages of infected foliage were: Phygon, 6 per cent; Bordeaux, 12 per cent; Fermate, 60 per cent; Dithane 75 per cent. In spite of the better control of blight by Phygon, this organic interfered with the metabolism of the plant.

Bordeaux dust is not effective unless applied to wet foliage. Otherwise the lime carbonates and will not form a protective film. Several dust preparations containing fixed or insoluble copper compounds are available. These can be applied when the foliage is dry and include those sold as tribasic copper, copper A, copper-oxychloride-sulfate (COCS), and yellow cuprocide. Tests comparing dusting with spraying have usually shown results somewhat in favor of spraying. Most dust materials are more expensive than spray materials,

Fig. 68. Applying Bordeaux dust with a dusting machine. Note fan type of nozzle.

but equipment for their application is less expensive. Blight can be effectively controlled by dusting, if the material is applied so as to give proper coverage. Usually it is necessary to use at least 25 to 30 pounds of dust to the acre.

Equipment, Materials, and Methods

Growers in high rainfall areas, especially where the nights are cool late in the growing season, should be equipped to control blight. Blight is more prevalent in the Northeast than in the South because in the South the nights are usually warm during the harvest season. Cool nights following warm days are necessary to germinate blight spores. In the semiarid west there is too little rainfall to favor the spread of blight. The problem of blight control in Kern

County, California, is difficult because ground equipment for spraying or dusting cannot be operated where the crop is irrigated in every other row on every other day. Since spraying is a protection and not a cure, the fungicide should be applied so thoroughly as to cover the upper surface of every leaflet before blight infection occurs. Very little, if any, infection occurs through the lower leaf surface, so it is not necessary to spray the lower side of the foliage.

Fig. 69. Dusting with a helicopter has the advantages of speed and getting the job done when ground is wet.

Many types and sizes of sprayers are now available. Size of pump and tank capacity vary according to acreage to be sprayed and number of rows to be covered at one time. The most modern sprayers are of the trailer type with the tank mounted behind the tractor and the sprayer boom ahead of the tractor. The larger sprayers carry a 10-row boom to spray 10 rows at a time with 3 nozzles to the row. Two of the three nozzles are set at an angle to cover the sides of the plants; the third nozzle is directly above to cover the top of the foliage. There are two types of nozzle arrangement—one known as the brush type with all nozzles at the same plane above the plants, the other known as the Nixon type in which the two side nozzles are on drop pipes to cover the lower part of the plant more thoroughly. A modern 10-row sprayer of the trailer type with brush type boom is shown in figure 65.

Pressure of application and the amount of material are factors which determine thoroughness of coverage. About 300 pounds' pressure at the nozzle is considered the minimum necessary, and at least 100 gallons of spray material to the acre are needed. For late-season coverage of the larger growing varieties, 125 gallons may be necessary. Pressure and type of nozzle largely determine the thoroughness of coverage, therefore, the nozzle discs and whirl plates should be renewed as the holes in them become worn too large. The various parts which make up a good spray nozzle are shown in figure 67.

The airplane and the helicopter have recently been adapted for applying fungicides and insecticides in dust form. They offer the advantage of quick coverage of large acreages, sometimes when the soil is too wet for ground equipment. Co-operative spray rings have been organized in several states to minimize the cost of spraying for many growers whose acreages are too small to justify the investment necessary for a satisfactory sprayer. Such rings usually consist of a group of growers who contract with the operator and owner of a power sprayer to spray a total of 150 to 200 acres made up of small individual units.

REFERENCES

Barrus, M. F., Charles Chupp, and K. H. Fernow. Potato diseases and their control. Cornell Extension Bul. 135, rev. 1940.

Blodgett, F. M., and F. B. Howe. Factors influencing the occurrence of potato scab in New York. Cornell Univ. Agr. Exp. Sta. Bul. 581, 1934.

Bonde, Reiner. Bacterial wilt and soft rot of the potato in Maine. Maine Agr. Exp. Sta. Bul. 396, 1939.

Cunningham, H. S., and W. F. Mai. Nematodes parasitic on the Irish potato. Cornell Extension Bul. 712, 1947.

Dykstra, T. P. Production of disease-free seed potatoes. U.S. Dept. Agr. Circ. 764, 1948.

Hansing, E. D. A study of the control of the yellow-dwarf disease of potatoes. Cornell Univ. Agr. Exp. Sta. Bul. 792, 1943.

Jensen, J. H., and J. E. Livingston. Potato diseases in Nebraska. Nebr. Agr. Exp. Sta. Bul. 378, 1945.

Libby, W. C., G. W. Simpson, and O. L. Wyman. Net necrosis of the potato. Maine Ext. Bul. 246, 1938.

Mills, W. R. The influence of maturity of potato varieties upon their susceptibility to late blight. Amer. Potato Jour. 15, No. 11, 1938.

Odland, Theodore E. Control of potato diseases. R.I. Agr. Exp. Sta., 58th Ann. Report, Contrib. 683, 1946.

Wilson, J. D., and H. A. Runnels. Effect on transpiration of varying the copper-lime ratio in Bordeaux mixtures. Ohio Agr. Exp. Sta. Bimonthly Bul. 20, 1935.

CHAPTER 10

Insects and Other Pests

DAMAGE to the potato crop by insects and the various types of animal pests is much less than that caused by diseases. This is partly because there are fewer of such pests and partly because they are more easily and cheaply controlled. Insects cause damage in two ways: by their direct effects on plant and tuber and by acting as vectors of diseases. The latter type of damage may be even more serious than the former. Examples may be found in the aphid as a carrier of mosaic and leaf roll, the clover leaf hopper as a carrier of yellow dwarf, the six-spotted leaf hopper as a vector of purple-top wilt, and the potato psyllid as a carrier of the psyllid yellows disease.

Classification

The more important potato insects can be grouped into various categories for the purpose of helping growers to understand and apply control measures. Those insects which affect the foliage are mainly the Colorado potato beetle, flea beetle, leaf hopper, aphid, blister beetle, tarnished plant bug, and the potato psyllid. Those most damaging to the tubers are the white grub, wireworm, slug, millipede, scab gnat, and the potato tuber worm. Another classification useful from the standpoint of control is that based on method of feeding. Sucking insects such as the aphid, leaf hopper, and tarnished plant bug are controlled by either contact insecticides or repellents, whereas leaf-eating insects must be controlled by the application of insecticides to the surface of the foliage.

Fig. 70. Colorado potato beetle and larva.

Diseases caused by insects and other pests which damage the tuber and the severity of which depends on soil conditions naturally must be controlled by methods other than spraying or dusting. Such methods can be grouped conveniently into three categories: (1) soil rotation, (2) regulation of soil reaction, and (3) soil fumigation. Rotation of crops, or choice of field and soil, is a practical means of reducing damage by wireworms, grubs, millipedes, and scab gnats. Inasmuch as millipedes and scab gnats feed on the lesions caused by common scab, control of them is mainly by keeping the soil reaction too acid for the development of scab. As explained in an earlier chapter, this may require the use of sulfur, or acidifying fertilizers, and avoidance of fresh stable manure. Recently soil fumigants have been developed for the control of wireworms. They may be expensive, and some of them impart a disagreeable odor and flavor to the potato tubers, but they are nevertheless very effective in ridding the soil of this pest.

Climatic Influences

Insects and other pests have a way of "building up" after the potato crop has been grown over a long period in any given region. Most of the well-known pests abound in the older producing areas such as Maine, New York, Pennsylvania, Michigan, and New Jersey. Comparatively few are found in Texas, California, and the Dakotas. The psyllid which transmits the psyllid yellows disease is seldom found outside the area of Colorado, Wyoming, Utah, and western Nebraska. Flea beetles and leaf hoppers are most damaging in hot dry seasons and areas. The aphis is prevalent from Maine to the Gulf States and is the insect most responsible for the spread of the more common virus diseases. Its effect on yield is obviously more pronounced from Long Island south than it is in regions farther north.

Important Insect and Other Pests

Many growers are unable to identify all of the more important insects that attack potatoes even though they have had long experience with the crop. Obviously it is difficult to aply appropriate control measures without some knowledge of the insects' appearance, feeding habits, life cycle, and method of overwintering. An easy way to find what insects are present is to beat them onto a white handkerchief placed between the rows. A brief discussion and an illustration of the more important pests are given here.

Aphids. The aphid or plant louse is a tiny green or pinkish insect which damages the potato plant both by sucking juices from the undersurface of the leaflet and by transmitting certain virus diseases. There are several kinds, but according to Shands *et al.* (1947) the three most common on potatoes are the potato aphid, *Macrosiphum solanifolii* (Ashm.), the green peach aphid, *Myzus persicae* (Sulz.), and the buckthorn aphid, *Aphis abbreviata* Patch. The two first named are probably the most widespread. Many kinds of weeds and shrubs, particularly the wild rose, serve as host plants from which

Fig. 71. Potato flea beetle.

these aphids migrate to potato fields in the form of winged females. The eradication of those weeds, especially from hedgerows border-ing the potato field, is one means of reducing the aphid population. The aphid is difficult to control because, once present in large numbers, it causes the leaflets to curl downward and is hard to hit with the necessary contact spray or dust. Effective control requires the application of nicotine sulfate spray or of DDT spray or dust to the underside of the foliage as early as the population is begin-ning to build up. A second application about a week later is also advised. The aphid is considered to be the most important vector of the leaf roll and the mosaic viruses.

Colorado Potato Beetle. This pest was known to infest fields east of the Rocky Mountains for many years. It gradually spread eastward from that area beginning about 90 years ago, but with modern con-trol methods it is no longer serious except in gardens where the crop is not well cared for. The Colorado potato beetle, *Leptinotarsa decemlineata* (Say), is a hard-shelled beetle of orange color, with ten black lines over its wing covers; it is about ¼ inch long. In large numbers the adult beetle may completely devour the foliage. However, the smaller, orange-colored slugs do most of the feeding early in the season in most fields. The adult overwinters in the soil at a depth of several inches. As it emerges, the female lays a clump of orange-yellow eggs on the underside of the leaves. The larvae or slugs, which hatch from these eggs, feed for about 3 weeks, then enter the ground to pupate. After about 5 to 10 days in the pupal stage, the adult emerges, and a second generation of eggs is laid. There are usually two generations a year. Control is by spraying or dusting with an insecticide on the surface of the leaves. DDT is very effective, but even Bordeaux mixture acts as a deterrent.

Flea Beetle, Epitrix cucumeris (Harris). The flea beetle is a hard-shelled, jet-black beetle which eats small pinholes in the leaflets in such numbers as, sometimes, to reduce yield and cause premature death of the plant. It is about $\frac{1}{16}$ inch in length, and when disturbed it hops away into hiding. The adult emerges from the soil early in the spring, and if not controlled it may completely destroy the young plant. After feeding for 3 or 4 weeks the beetles enter the soil to lay eggs. Tiny white worms hatch and soon emerge again as beetles to feed on the foliage as a second generation in August. The late brood of worms feeds on grass roots and sometimes punctures the new tubers to form a sliverlike defect just under the skin. Bordeaux spray is effective as a repellent, and DDT added to the mixture about every two weeks almost completely eliminates this pest.

The Western potato flea beetle, *Epitrix subcrinita* (Leconte), is a serious pest in the Rocky Mountain and northwestern states. The larvae feed on the developing tubers, causing small "tracks" and "slivers" which sometimes seriously deform the tubers and lower their marketability.

Leaf Hopper, Empoasca fabae (Harris). Until the advent of DDT in the potato spray program, damage to the potato plant by the leaf

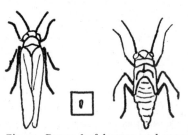

hopper was probably more extensive than that by any other foliage insect. The leaf hopper is a yellowish green insect about $\frac{1}{8}$ inch long and fashioned like a grasshopper. It feeds by sucking the undersurface of the leaflets, and in large numbers it causes a drying-out of the tissue, evident

Fig. 72. Potato leaf hopper and nymph.

on the edge of the leaflet, called "hopper burn." Growers often mistake this injury for late blight. The adult over-winters under brush heaps and trash and after feeding for a week or so migrates to the potato field. There are two generations in the northern states, more than this in the South. Control is the same as for the flea beetle, except that the spray or dust should be applied to the underside of the foliage. The effectiveness of leaf hoppers in reducing the yield and the starch content of potato tubers is such that Apple and

Arnold (1945) reported the extent of damage in a control experiment in terms of differences in specific gravity of the tubers.

Tarnished Plant Bug, Lygus oblineatus (Say). This is one of the less important insect pests which affects the foliage only. It derives its name from the peculiar grayish-brown pattern of its wing covers. The adult is about $\frac{1}{8}$ inch long and very elusive. When disturbed its habit is to crawl quickly from the upper to the lower surface of the leaflet for hiding. Damage is largely through its feeding on the tender new growth tips at the top of the plant. It feeds by puncturing the veins of the leaflet and sucking the juices, after which its presence is noted in the wilted and dead growth tips. Only when present in great numbers and uncontrolled is it likely to cause an appreciable reduction in yield. It is effectively repelled by an application of Bordeaux mixture and easily controlled with the addition of DDT as an insecticide.

Psyllid, Paratrioza cockerelli (Sulc.). The potato psyllid is the insect responsible for the psyllid yellows disease sometimes damaging to the crop in Colorado, Montana, western Nebraska, New Mexico, Utah, and Wyoming. It is a sucking insect, the adults of which have been described as small "jumping plant lice." The tiny, scalelike, flat nymphs suck juice from shaded parts of the foliage, producing rolled or cupped, yellow or reddish leaflets, killing or stunting the plants and causing small malformed, unmarketable potatoes. Other effects on the plant

Fig. 73. Potato aphid.

include a tendency to develop axillary branches, aerial tubers, a pyramidal form of foliage, rosetting of the smaller, newer leaves, and several small tubers on each underground stolon. Damage is most severe when the attack on the plant is early or before the tubers form. Although the potato psyllid transmits the yellows disease in a manner similar to that of the aphid in transmitting virus, the yellows disease is not carried into succeeding generations through the seed tuber. However, affected tubers usually produce weak plants. Control is principally by spraying or dusting of the plants. Bordeaux mixture spray acts as a repellent, but insecticides are more effective. Spraying with lime-sulfur-zinc-arsenite has given good control. Lime sulfur and wettable sulfur sprays and sulfur dusts have been widely used. More recently DDT has proved to be the most effective and most economical insecticide for use against this pest.

Millipede, Julus coeruleocinctus Wood. A defect of potato tubers sometimes referred to as pitted scab may be caused by the millipede or "thousand-legged" worm. The millipede is a bluish-brown, wormlike pest about ¾ inch long when full grown, bearing many pairs of legs. It is coiled tightly when at rest. Although most of its feeding is on decaying vegetable matter and micro-organisms, its jaw parts are suited to feeding on the potato tuber. Its feeding there is most often associated with lesions of common scab which it deepens into shallow clean pits with no overhanging skin. Much of the injury is done by very young millipedes. According to MacLeod and Rawlins (1933) heavy applications of stable manure favor the prevalence of this pest. Since manure and scab are associated, it can be assumed that the best control measures are those commonly advised for the control of scab.

Fig. 74. Tarnished plant bug.

Scab gnat, Pnyxia scabiei (Hopk.). This insect is found generally throughout the older potato states. In common with the millipede, the larva of the potato scab gnat often causes pitted scab. The female of the tiny adult fly or gnat deposits eggs either in decaying vegetable matter or in potato tissue injured by common scab or otherwise. From these eggs hatch very tiny white larvae which feed on the scabby tissue and deepen it into a pit. This type of pitted scab can be distinguished from millipede injury in that a black "frass," the excrement from the maggots, is left in the bottom of the pit. According to Gui (1933), the scab gnat overwinters in any moist situation, even in a potato cellar or in the field. It may even damage the stand of potatoes by feeding on the seed piece or the young plant. Further damage after infested potatoes are placed in storage is possible as the maggots continue to feed. Control measures include the use of clean seed, seed treatment, crop rotation, and such regulation of soil reaction as will best control scab.

Slug, Agriolimax agrestis Linn. The slug or "snail without a shell" does most of its damage by feeding on tubers grown in gardens and in the wetter areas of potato fields. It is seldom destructive where there is no excess moisture. It eats out large cavities in the tuber, but consumes little or none of the skin covering. The ragged edges of a slug cavity make it easily distinguishable from the damage done by millipedes and white grubs. Differences in the type of injury done by these three pests are well illustrated by MacLeod and Rawlins (1933) (see Chapter 11). This pest is not serious in commercial production, but in gardens control sometimes justifies the use of poison baits placed under shingles or boards.

Potato Tuber Worm, Gnorimoschema operculella (Zell.) The tuber worm is neither widespread nor universally serious; however, it became established in California, Florida, Virginia, and a few other states many years ago. Only occasionally are there outbreaks of serious consequence. The adult moth, similar to the Angoumois grain moth, is from $\frac{3}{8}$ to $\frac{1}{2}$ inch in length. Although it is the worm or larva which damages both foliage and tuber, the moth deposits eggs in protected places on any portion of the potato plant, infesting mainly plants of the Solanaceae family. Damage by the worm is by tunneling and rolling the leaflets and by tunneling through the tubers. In the field the plant may be almost completely killed, while in storage the tubers may be made worthless. According to Spencer and Strong (1925), the life cycle averages about 25 days in summer, longer in spring, and several months in winter. The adult over-winters in potato refuse piles, in stored potatoes, and in storage equipment. Control measures consist of fumigation of stored tubers with carbon bisulfide or with hydrocyanic acid gas, protection of the newly harvested crop by early marketing and coverage of barrels in the field, and observance of sanitary conditions to prevent over-wintering.

White Grub, Phyllophaga spp. Many are familiar with the great numbers of May beetles or June bugs which assemble around street lights and on lighted porches in early spring. These flights are most noticeable every third year when another generation of adult beetles is migrating to some congenial place to mate and lay eggs. Davis (1922) reported a very severe infestation of white grubs in 1912 and again in 1915. Similar infestations have occurred, though not all as severe, every third year since. Damage by white grubs to potato tubers was especially bad in 1941 and 1944 but less so in 1947. The white grub is the larva of the May beetle, which has a 3-year life cycle. Two whole years and a part of the third are spent as grubs in the soil. Most of the injury to corn roots and potato tubers is done during the second grub year when large cavities are eaten in the tuber. Corresponding to the size of the full-grown grub, which is over an inch long and a quarter-inch in diameter, the damage can be severe and may disqualify the tuber from No. 1 grade. White grubs are of economic importance to the industry in certain so-called grub areas throughout the north central and the middle Atlantic states. The beetle infests particularly old grass sod.

Best control of the white grub is to avoid planting potatoes on grass sod older than one year in areas regularly infested. Clover and other legumes should precede potatoes, as the grubs seldom feed on legume roots. Fall plowing to expose the grubs to winter freezing is not effective because the larvae go below the plowline before the advent of freezing temperatures.

Wireworms. The adult of the wireworm is the common click beetle or "snapping bug." It is as prevalent as the white grub and

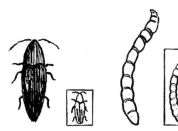

fully as damaging to the potato crop. Its larvae, known as wireworms because of their long, hard, cylindrical bodies, eat their way deeply into the tuber, often rendering it totally unfit for use. The life cycle is 3 to 5 years, 3 of which are spent in the soil as larva, the fourth as an adult beetle capable of flying

Fig. 75. Wireworm: adult beetle, larva.

long distances. The larva varies from ¼ to 1 inch in length depending on its age.

The types or species of wireworms which affect potato tubers vary in different regions. In the Pacific Northwest, including Idaho, two species are especially damaging. These are the Pacific Coast wireworm, *Limonius canus* (Lec.), and the sugar beet wireworm, *Limonius californicus* (Mann). For the control of these, it is recommended that soil insecticides be used. In the Red River Valley, the most damaging wireworm is *Ctenicera aereipennis destructor* (Brown), commonly called prairie grain wireworm. It too requires a soil insecticide for effective control. The potato soils of the southeastern coastal plain area, especially in the Carolinas, Georgia, and Alabama, are infested with still a different kind, it is the sand wireworm, *Horistonotus uhlereii* Horn. To rid infested soils of the sand wireworm, two or three years of sod or small grains should be planted before potatoes. Soil insecticides are also recommended, but best choice of these is not yet determined.

Three species of wireworms are usually found in damaging numbers in potato fields in the northeastern states and Canada. These, in order of importance, are the wheat wireworm, *Agriotes mancus* (Say), the eastern field wireworm, *Limonius agonus* (Say), and the corn wireworm, *Melanotus communis* Gyll. Although all three of these occur in greater numbers in low, wet areas than in high, dry ones, the wheat wireworm is more sensitive to soil moisture than are the others. While the wheat wireworm is most damaging to potatoes where the crop is planted on old sod, the eastern field type prefers the drier, sandier soils previously in some cultivated crop. Accordingly, control measures vary with the species of wireworm concerned. According to Rawlins (1940), the wheat wireworm adult lays its eggs in any crop which provides a good ground cover during the egg-laying period, usually May 1 to June 15 in western New York. A standard rotation of 3 or 4 years consisting of either potatoes, grain, clover, or potatoes, grain, clover, timothy, can be expected to keep the soil continuously infested. A cultivated crop following potatoes for at least two years will usually rid the soil of this pest. To avoid the wheat wireworm, potatoes should not be planted on land which was in sod during the egg-laying period of the previous two years.

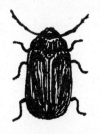

Fig. 76. White grub: adult beetle, larva.

The eastern field wireworm, which has recently become a serious pest of potatoes grown continuously on certain areas of Long Island, New York, and in New Jersey, must be controlled by soil fumigation. Soil fumigants are usually very expensive, and those most promising are still very much in the experimental stage. Among these are benzene hexachloride which, although very effective, if used in too large quantities imparts a disagreeable odor and flavor to the potato crop. Campbell (1924) reported favorable results with calcium cyanide dust as a soil fumigant. About 200 pounds to the acre killed about 70 per cent of the wireworms at the cost of about

$30 per acre. He claimed that the benefits would last two or three years.

Damage from wireworms can be reduced by harvesting the infested crop early to prevent further loss. This fact was substantiated by Hawkins (1937), who harvested one portion of the crop about a month earlier than another, with results shown in table 48.

TABLE 48. RELATION OF TIME OF HARVEST TO WIREWORM INJURY.

Date Harvested	Percentage of Tubers Injured	Injuries per 100 Tubers
September 12--15	27.5	129
October 14--16	42.3	340

Soil infestation was 44 per square yard, the same in each of the lots reported in the table above.

Insecticides

Methods of controlling insects and other animal pests must necessarily depend on where they attack the plant and their feeding habits. Chewing or leaf-eating insects can be killed by applying a poison to the surface of the leaf. Sucking insects are controlled partly by the use of contact insecticides and partly by repellents. Pests which feed on the underground parts of the potato plant must be controlled by such means as soil fumigants and crop rotation. The appropriate type or types of control have been indicated in the discussion of each pest above. For the exact insecticide, formula, and rate and method of application, it is always best to follow the latest directions and advice of the nearest and most authoritative extension agency. One of the best sources of information on fungicides and insecticides, with their formulation and application for all types of vegetable crops, is that of Chupp and Leiby (1948).

Arsenicals, one of the oldest forms of insecticides, are very effective against leaf-eating insects. Calcium arsenate applied with Bordeaux as a spray for the control of Colorado beetles, flea beetles, and leaf hoppers was extensively used until DDT was developed. Bordeaux mixture either as a spray or a dust is of insecticidal value mainly as a repellent. However, its lime content affects different insects in different ways. Apparently, as the ratio of lime to copper increases, flea beetles and hoppers are repelled and aphids are attracted. Nicotine in the form of nicotine sulfate spray with a soap emulsion applied to the underside of potato leaves is one of the best controls for the potato aphid. It is less effective when applied with Bordeaux mixture.

Neither rotenone, rotenone-bearing dusts, nor pyrethrum dusts are much used as potato insecticides. They are more expensive than arsenicals and DDT and perform no more useful function.

The relatively new insecticide DDT (abbreviation of dichloro-

Fig. 77. White grubs feeding on potato tubers. (Entomology Dept., Cornell Univ.)

diphenyl-trichloroethane) is the most widely useful control of nearly all potato insects yet developed. Furthermore it has the effect of keeping potato foliage alive enough longer to increase the yield significantly over plants treated with other insecticides. It is relatively nonpoisonous to man, but on the nervous system of cold-blooded insects it has a paralyzing effect which lasts several days. The only important potato foliage insect not fully controlled by proper application of DDT is the aphid. As is true with nicotine sulfate, it is only partly effective against this pest and must be applied in extra large dosages or increased concentrations. It is incompatible with copper-lime dust and should not be mixed with it because lime tends to lessen the potency of the insecticide. DDT can be bought as a 50-per-cent wettable powder, a 40-per-cent wettable powder, or a 25-per-cent wettable powder, but mixed with water or Bordeaux it should be used in an amount that will apply about 1 pound of actual DDT to the acre or to each 100 gallons of spray. Usually a 3-per-cent DDT dust is applied to potato foliage at the rate of 25 to 30 pounds to the acre. Growers usually find it necessary to apply DDT only every other week while insects are present. Muncie and Morofsky (1947), in experiments conducted in Michigan during 1938–1945, obtained higher potato yields from plants sprayed with high lime Bordeaux plus DDT than from plants sprayed with fixed coppers and DDT. However, DDT added to fixed coppers gave higher yields than did any other insecticide so added. DDT gave better control of leaf hoppers, flea beetles, and aphids than did Bordeaux mixture, tribasic copper, sulfate-zinc sulfate-lime, yellow cuprocide, or Dithane-DDD (dichloro-diphenyl-dichloroethane).

Another of the newer insecticides which shows particular promise against all common potato insects is parathion, O, O-diethyl O-p-nitrophenyl thiophosphate. One of its special advantages is its effectiveness against aphids. Like DDT, it has considerable residual value, but unlike DDT it is more dangerous to handle. Growers using it should take the precaution to wear a respirator.

It is not always practical to eliminate wireworms from the soil by crop rotation. For a quicker and more thorough method, soil fumigants are useful. Four soil insecticides have been tried more or less experimentally. These are D-D, ethylene dibromide, benzene-hexachloride, and chlordane. Benzene hexachloride (BHC) and chlordane are both hydrocarbons quite toxic to wireworms. They can be applied to the soil as sprays or dusts. The former has given some trouble by imparting a disagreeable odor or flavor to potato tubers.

REFERENCES

Apple, James W. and Charles Y. Arnold. The use of tuber specific gravity in determining the effectiveness of leafhopper insecticides. Amer. Potato Jour. 22, No. 11, 1945.

Campbell, Roy E. Preliminary report on the use of calcium cyanide as a soil fumigant for wireworms. Jour. Econ. Entom., 17, 1924.

Chupp, Charles, and R. W. Leiby. The control of diseases and insects affecting vegetable crops. Cornell Ext. Bul. 206, 1948.

Davis, John J. Common white grubs. U.S. Dept. Agr. Farmers' Bul. 940, 1922.

Gui, Harry L. The potato scab-gnat, *Pnyxia scabiei* (Hopkins). Ohio Agr. Exp. Sta. Bul. 524, 1933.

Hawkins, John H. Wireworm control for Maine potato growers. Amer. Potato Jour., 14, No. 11, 1937.

MacLeod, G. F., and W. A. Rawlins. Insect and other injuries to potato tubers. Cornell Univ. Agr. Exp. Sta. Bul. 569, 1933.

Muncie, J. H., and W. F. Morofsky. Results of spraying and dusting with fungicides and insecticides on potatoes, 1938–45. Mich. Agr. Exp. Sta. Tech. Bul. 204, 1947.

Rawlins, W. A. Biology and control of the wheat wireworm, *Agriotes Mancus* Say. Cornell Univ. Agr. Exp. Sta. Bul. 738, 1940.

Shands, W. A., G. W. Simpson, C. M. Flynn, P. H. Lung, and B. A. Seaman. Biology and control of aphids affecting potatoes in Maine. Maine Agr. Exp. Sta. Bul. 449, 1947.

Spencer, Herbert, and W. O. Strong. The potato tuber worm. Va. Truck Exp. Sta. Bul. 53, 1925.

Thomas, C. A. The biology and control of wireworms. Pa. Agr. Exp. Sta. Bul. 392, 1940.

CHAPTER 11

Tuber Defects

T HE NUMBER and the diversity of types of defects to which
the potato tuber is subject are suprisingly large. Some of these
are of only minor importance, others are so serious as to involve
great financial loss to the grower every year. Without exception,
they detract from the appearance and therefore the market quality
of the crop. Certain types render the tuber worthless for culinary
purposes, others result in a lowering of the market grade. More than
one-half of the total known defects are caused by factors other than
diseases and insects. A better knowledge of the nature, causes, and
control of these defects should be of benefit to growers, handlers,
and consumers. The first step in improvement of market quality in
potatoes is a recognition of the defects which degrade them.

Classification

Defects of potato tubers can be classified, for convenience, into
six types according to the nature of the causal factor. They are as
follows:

Animal Pests
  Mole
  Mouse
  Pheasant
  Rat
Diseases
  Bacterial soft rot (blackleg)
  Brown rot
  Fusarium dry rot
  Internal brown spot (caused by
    F. eumartii, yellow dwarf,
    sprain)

Jelly-end rot (leak)
Late blight
Net necrosis
Rhizoctonia (black scurf)
Root knot nematode
Russet scab
Scab
Silver scurf
Stem-end browning
Vascular discoloration
Insects
  Flea beetle

Insects (cont.)
  Grub
  Millipede
  Scab gnat
  Slug
  Wireworm
Mechanical
  Bruises
  Cuts
  Pressure bruises
  Skinning
Miscellaneous
  Fertilizer injury
  Quack grass or nut grass
Physiological
  Air cracks

Black heart
Enlarged lenticels
Freezing injury
Frost necrosis
Growth cracks
Hollow heart
Internal roots
Internal tubers
Misshape
Second growth
Shriveling
Sprouting
Sprout tubers
Sunburn
Sunscald

Characteristics, Cause, and Control

The nature of tuber defects is best learned by study of actual material. The student will not ordinarily find it difficult to assemble a large proportion of the 46 defects listed in the above classification for study. For help in such a study, a brief discussion of each defect and an illustration of several of the more important ones are given in this chapter.

Animal Pests

Animal pests that feed on potato tubers are few and usually of only minor importance. They consist mostly of rodents and birds. The *field mouse* is sometimes damaging in fields where the soil is loose, and where there are enough old sod, grass, and weeds to provide cover. Both field mice and *moles* feed on tubers late in the season and are more numerous in muck than in upland soils. *Pheasants* do considerable damage in fields near hedgerows, especially to tubers not well covered. The tooth marks of mice and moles can be distinguished from pheasant injury by their smaller, more regular striations. *Rats* may do even more damage to potatoes in storage, especially in the absence of other feed. Their tooth marks are larger than those of mice, and they leave numerous pieces of the tuber strewn about. Best control is to ratproof the storage place and to use poison bait.

Diseases

Of the many disease organisms which injure potato tubers, the majority affect the flesh and therefore the internal quality. The two which directly cause soft rot are *bacterial soft rot* and *brown rot*. The former usually follows tuber bruises when affected tubers are stored in moist storage. It may also be the direct result of infection with blackleg at the stem end of the tuber. Brown rot is a bacterial soft rot which infects newly harvested potatoes in the

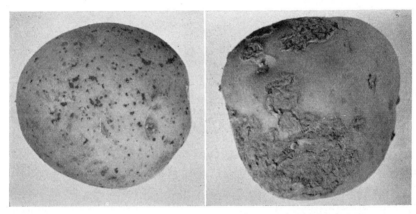

Fig. 78. Rhizoctonia or black scurf.   *Fig. 79.* Scab.

South when they are bruised or skinned and later stored and shipped under high temperatures before being thoroughly dried. *Fusarium dry rot* is the common form of dry rot which starts with any form of mechanical injury and may envelop the whole tuber. It develops mostly in storage, and certain varieties, notably Sebago, are especially susceptible. *Internal brown spot* is a defect which consists of tiny brown necrotic spots throughout the internal tissue. Although it renders the tuber worthless for cooking, its exact cause is difficult to determine. In England and in Canada it is called *sprain* and is classed as a physiological disease. In the United States it is said to be due either to a form of wilt, *Fusarium eumartii,* or to *yellow dwarf.* The variety Erie is especially susceptible to this defect, and no control is known except to grow such varieties as are resistant to it. *Jelly-end rot* is a defect found mostly in the Netted

Gem or Russet Burbank variety grown in Idaho. It produces a soft rot at the stem end of the tuber, and shipments of potatoes during warm weather sometimes arrive in a leaky condition. The defect is usually then referred to as *leak*. The only control known is to observe careful handling. *Late blight* causes irregular sunken areas on the surface of the tuber and, when the tuber is cut transversely, a reddish brown dry rot extending inward no further than the vascular ring can be observed. Although late blight seldom develops further in storage, it may give ready access to other rot-producing organisms. Naturally the control is to protect the growing

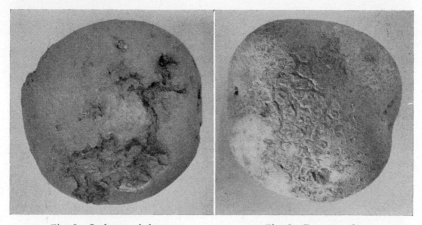

Fig. 80. Scab-gnat injury.   *Fig. 81.* Russet scab.

plant from this disease. *Net necrosis* is well described by its name in that a network of necrotic tissue ramifies the flesh of the tuber. Its presence is associated with current-season infection of the plant with the leaf roll disease. Like internal brown spot, it may continue its development in storage and thereby destroy the value of the tuber for market. Control is to prevent plant infection with the leaf roll virus. *Rhizoctonia,* better known as black scurf, disfigures the tuber by the coal-black patches of dried mycelium on the skin. Since it does not penetrate the flesh, the injury is confined to the appearance of the tuber. The *root-knot nematode,* one of the eel-worm diseases, produces a rough knotty surface so bad as to make the tuber unsalable. Although the defect can be readily peeled away, it is usually serious enough to render the tuber worthless for market. This defect is found in only a few areas, hence is of minor importance (for control, see Chapter 9). The defect called *russet scab* is also usually not serious and only disfigures the skin of the tuber. Its pattern is somewhat like checkerboard markings in patches which somewhat resemble scab but are not so deep. It has not been determined whether it is caused by rhizoctonia, by fertilizer injury,

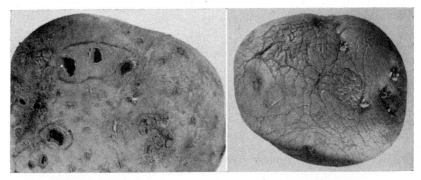

Fig. 82. Millipede injury.   *Fig. 83.* Silver scurf.

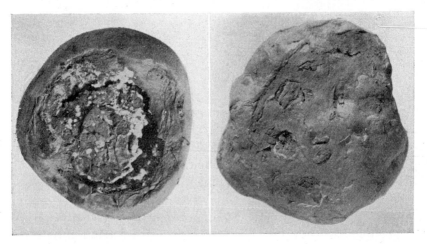

Fig. 84. Bacterial soft rot.   *Fig. 85.* Late blight dry rot. Note reddish brown decay.

or some other agency. *Scab* is probably the most common tuber defect caused by disease. It occurs as very irregular-shaped lesions, varying in depth from superficial to an eighth of an inch and filled with rough, dry skin tissue (control is discussed in Chapter 9). *Silver scurf* appears in irregular-shaped silvery patches of skin and is in fact confined to the skin. It can damage the tuber only in appearance, and it is especially noticeable in smooth, glossy-skinned varieties such as Cobbler, Houma, Chippewa, and Katahdin. It is caused by the fungus *Spondylocladium atrovirens* and is favored by moist soil and humid storage. In storage it may increase weight loss by accelerating the loss of moisture. Control is by seed treatment. *Stem-end browning,* sometimes called mahogany browning, is one of the more common and serious defects which appears at the stem end of the tuber. It may increase in depth and intensity of color after harvest, so that damage may affect both grade and culinary value. It is probably caused by toxic substances translocated from the living stem of the plant. Several factors influence its development, and some varieties are more susceptible than others. The Green Mountain variety has given much trouble with this defect in Maine. Ross (1945) reported that late plantings, early harvest, increasing the fertilizer and the amount of potash in the fertilizer, as well as the amount of chlorine, all tended to increase the severity of stem-end browning. Premature killing of the plant to facilitate harvest has also been shown to aggravate this trouble. Potatoes predisposed to stem-end browning should be stored at temperatures below 50° F., as that temperature has been found by Ross to check development of the disease. *Vascular discoloration* is a common defect by which the vascular ring at the stem end of the tuber is necrotic. The resulting black or brown ring is unsightly and may be serious in the cooked product. It is caused mainly by the fungus *Fusarium oxysporum,* a wilt producing organism, the control of which is discussed in Chapter 9.

Insect Pests

The number of insect pests which cause injury to potato tubers is much less than that of diseases. Some of these pests may invade only the surface tissue and cause damage in appearance; others may bore deeply and involve serious damage. *Flea beetle* injury is usually not serious and becomes noticeable only in dry seasons when little or no spray is applied to the plant. Then the larva penetrates into the cortical layer causing a sliverlike defect which is easily removed by peeling. Control is by the use of DDT or other insecticides. Damage by the *grub* is often serious in grub years in areas subject to this pest. Here the larva of the May beetle eats large cavities into the tuber, leaving no residue and no skin remnant around the edges of the affected area. In severe cases, tubers may be largely consumed and even the stand of plants reduced. Control requires care in selecting the field to be planted, especially in grub years. The *millipede* feeds mostly on scabby or otherwise injured tubers, causing what is often called pitted scab. These pits are much

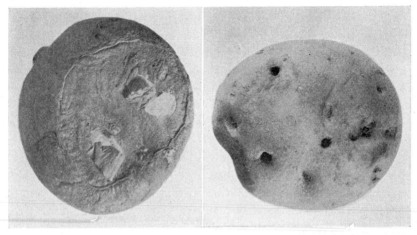

Fig. 86. Freezing injury. Note patch of white starch under skin.

Fig. 87. Wireworm injury.

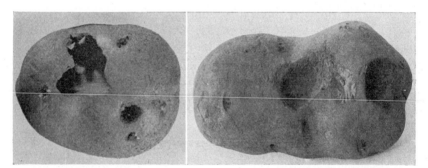

Fig. 88. Slug or snail injury.

Fig. 89. Grub injury. (Entomology Dept., Cornell Univ.)

smaller than those made by grubs, and they are usually confined to the areas occupied originally by scab lesions. Damage can be reduced by harvesting the infested crop early and by controlling scab. *Scab-gnat* injury is another form of pitted scab easily recognized by the black residue left by the larva, or tiny white maggots which feed on scab lesions. The cavity is even deeper than that caused

by millipedes, and the injury is most severe on potatoes grown in
soil containing much decaying organic matter. *Slug* or snail injury
is of little economic importance, but in gardens it may seem serious.
It consists of deep cavities about the same in depth and extent as
grub injury, but with the difference that the skin is not eaten.
Of all the insects which feed on potatoes, *wireworms* probably are
most serious. All three species previously described sometimes leave
an otherwise good crop of tubers badly damaged by deep tunnels.
Two or three wireworm holes, if deep enough, are sufficient to disqualify a tuber from No. 1 grade. Most of the damage is done by
1-year-old larvae which leave holes about the diameter of the lead in
a lead pencil, extending from ½ to ¾ of an inch deep. Damage done
by worms in their second year is usually less extensive in that the
feeding is done early when the tubers are small, and, as the tuber
enlarges, the hole is widened to leave superficial scar tissue. Control
of wireworms is discussed in Chapter 10.

Mechanical Injury

A sad commentary on the potato industry is the fact that many
of the best crops are grown only to be seriously damaged in the
process of harvesting. Of all the defects found in potatoes sold in
retail stores in our cities, more than one-half are bruises and cuts. Mechanical injury, more than any other single defect, is responsible for
putting market potatoes out of grade. The greater part of this injury
is done as the tubers pass over the digger. *Shatter bruises* occur when
too little soil is carried on the digger chain to cushion the tubers
against rotating iron rods. Field studies by Hardenburg and Turner
(1940) showed that from 0.75 to 15.0 per cent of tubers are bruised
on the digger depending on the type of digger and how it is equipped
and operated. Other workers have reported bruising as high as 40
to 50 per cent in potatoes examined behind the digger. Such bruises
need be only enough skin abrasion to allow juice to escape and rot organisms to penetrate and cause rot. *Cracking* may occur in potatoes
harvested when immature and very turgid or brittle. Cracking and
shatter bruises result from both digging and subsequent handling.
Bruising can be greatly reduced by carrying more soil on the digger
chain, by eliminating most of the agitation, by removal of chain rods
to eliminate the slack, by slower operation of the chain, and by
padding the rear guards. *Cuts* are caused mostly by the digger point

which slices the tubers. A clean cut may heal if the tuber is stored in a fairly warm moist place, and, in such case, the loss may not be serious. To avoid cuts, the digger point should be set deeper. *Skinning* or "feathering" is a defect common to potatoes harvested when very immature. It makes the tubers look ragged, but unless

Fig. 90. Mouse injury.   Fig. 91. Sunburn.

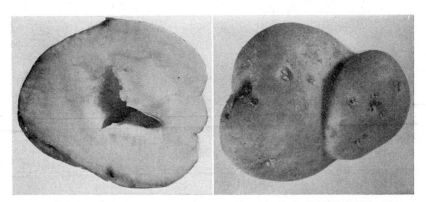

Fig. 92. Hollow heart.   Fig. 93. Misshape.

they are subjected to hot sun and scalding, the damage is small. When skinned potatoes are exposed to intense sunlight at high temperatures they may turn black and even develop a soft, slimy rot. Skinning can be reduced by allowing the tubers to dry an hour before picking and by careful handling all the way through the marketing process. Good illustrations of mechanically injured tubers are shown by Hastings (1932) and by Schrumpf (1933).

Cracking is fully discussed and illustrated by Werner (1931). *Pressure bruises* are of two types: that caused by excess piling in storage or in the car, and that found more recently on Long Island which results in a blackish or bluish spot just under the skin. Damage from pressure bruising does not require that the skin be actually broken. Exact cause of damage by internal black spot has not been determined, but the best safeguard against it is careful handling in and out of storage.

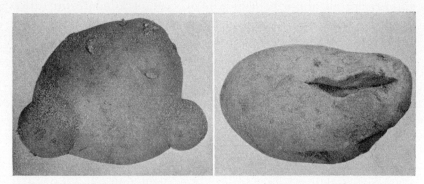

Fig. 94. Second growth.   Fig. 95. Growth cracks.

Fig. 96. Skinning.   Fig. 97. Digger cut.

Miscellaneous Defects

Included in this category are those rather rare abnormalities which do not appropriately fit into any of the other five classifications. Certain of the perennial grasses such as *quack grass, Agropyron repens,* and *nut grass, Cyperus rotundus,* produce underground stems or rhizomes which penetrate potato tubers, causing some waste when the tubers are prepared for cooking. In the case of nut grass, torpedo-shaped tubers or "nuts" form at the nodes of the rhizomes. When the rhizome penetrates the tuber, these nuts are sometimes left inside to cause damage to the harvested crop. Control of nut grass is especially difficult, but continuous summer fallowing for three years to dry out and starve the rhizomes and nuts seems to offer most promise until chemical weedicides have been developed. *Internal roots, internal tubers,* and *inverted sprouts* are all abnormalities which occur occasionally in tubers stored overlong under conditions favorable for sprouting. None of these is of economic importance. Hardenburg (1940) reported the occurrence of internal roots in Bliss Triumph potatoes stored over the summer in a house cellar. The roots originated at the base of the apical sprout just beneath the periderm and penetrated to the base of the tuber through the inner medulla (see figure 101). Internal sprouts and internal tubers, or tubers within tubers, are the result of growth of inverted sprouts within old tubers held in moist storage. These are illustrated in figures 99 and 100. In occasional years when potato seed pieces have been planted in soil unfavorable for rapid sprout growth, an abnormality called *sprout tubers* develops. This is not due to a disease, nor is it the result of faulty seed, even though the grower usually thinks so. When the soil is excessively cold or dry after planting, sprout growth may be retarded for several weeks. As a result, new daughter tubers may form at the eyes of the parent seed, or a chain of new tubers may develop successively on the stolon (see figure 102). This situation is interesting in that a new crop is produced without benefit of top growth, but the stand is poor and the yield seriously reduced. Weiss and Brierley (1926) found that seed potatoes stored at fairly high temperatures and later desprouted four or five times have a tendency to produce sprout tubers when planted in cold, dry soil. Sprout tubers are sometimes formed late in the growth period if the soil temperature is high. In this case, the effect of the high soil temperature is to hasten breakage of the rest period and to stimulate sprout growth before the crop is harvested.

Physiological Defects

These include all defects not directly the result of animal, insect, disease, and weed pests, and mechanical injury. The list is rather long. These defects invariably are the result of unfavorable growth or storage environment. Individually only a few of them are usually very serious, collectively they involve considerable loss and must be removed in grading for market. *Air cracks* are crescent-shaped checks in the skin which result when tubers are removed from a low-temperature, humid storage to a warm room. It is the result of rapid drying of the skin and somewhat disfigures exhibit potatoes. *Blackheart* is a black decay at the center of the tuber resulting from suboxidation or asphyxiation in storage. It may occur in tubers

Fig. 98. Shatter bruise.   Fig. 99. Adventitious sprout
                                  in cut surface of tuber.

close to heaters placed in bulk carlot shipments to protect against freezing in transit. It is not likely to occur in storage where provision for air circulation is adequate. *Enlarged lenticels* sometimes disfigure potato tubers harvested from excessively wet soil. Waterlogged soil provides too little air for normal respiration and as a result the lenticels extrude. Varieties with prominent lenticels, such as Early Ohio and Sebago, are especially susceptible. *Freezing injury* occurring either before or after harvest may assume any one of many forms. If the tuber is completely frozen, the cells will rupture, and wet breakdown follows. Injury not sufficient to cause cell rupture may cause various forms of black discoloration in any portion of the tuber. Affected areas may resemble net necrosis (in which case the defect is called *frost necrosis*), or they may resemble blotches of varying degrees of intensity. *Growth cracks* are seldom deep enough to disqualify potatoes for No. 1 grade. They are caused by rapid expansion of the inner portion of the tuber following a check in growth caused by drought. Varieties of the Rural type appear to be especially susceptible. *Hollow heart* is a rupture in the pith tissue of the tuber which, if large or discolored, makes the tuber worthless for cooking. Its cause is not definitely known, but it is associated with rapid growth and oversized tubers. Werner (1927) found over 60 per cent of one lot of Russet Rural potatoes affected with this defect. He also found it to be very closely associated with growth cracks and oversize, again indicating that it is at least in part due to rapid growth. Werner was able to reduce hollow heart by treating the seed with thiourea to increase stem numbers in the

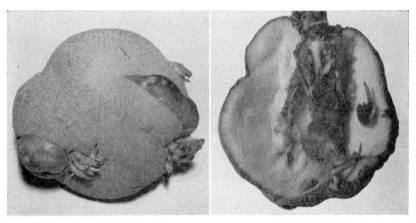

Fig. 100. Internal tubers from inverted sprouts. (Edgar I. Schauber, Ballston Lake, N.Y.)

Fig. 101. Internal roots from base of apical sprout.

plant and thereby reduce tuber size. Close spacing of seed is another means of control. The Cobbler, Rural, and Sequoia varieties are especially subject to this defect. An entire crop of Cobbler has been known to be affected, even the smallest tubers. *Misshape* and *second growth* defects are very common in such varieties as Early Ohio, Russet Burbank, and Rural. Green Mountain is often badly affected with misshaped tubers, resulting when secondary growth at the eyes causes knobs to form. Other malformations involving dumbbells, pointed ends, and creases are classed as misshape. Misshape is most common in potatoes grown in heavy soils. Second growth may occur when growth of tuber is resumed after a dry period. *Shriveling* and *sprouting* occur in warm storage favorable to excessive sprout growth and moisture loss. They are classed as condition factors by market inspectors and sometimes result in disqualification from No. 1 grade. Next to bruises, *sunburn* is the most serious defect found in market potatoes. It is the result of exposure of tubers to sunlight before harvest and, depending on the area affected and the intensity of greenness, may make the tuber worthless for eating. The defective portion contains not only chlorophyll but also the alkaloid solanine. Eaten in excess, it is likely to be toxic to the digestive tract. Sunburned tubers, however, are suitable for

Fig. 102. Sprout tubers resulting from old seed stored in damp cellar or from delayed germination after planting.

seed, and the defect is not transmitted to the following crop. Varieties, such as Katahdin, which set shallow are especially susceptible. Deeper planting and ridge culture are aids to control of the defect. *Sunscald* is a result of exposure of newly harvested, immature tubers to intense sunlight immediately after harvest. To prevent it, southern potato growers cover the tubers with potato tops or move them immediately to storage. Badly scalded tubers are flaccid, pale yellowish in color, and often unfit for storage or use.

Distinguishing Characteristics

The student will find it useful to be able to distinguish certain of the above defects most likely to be confused. Among these defects are the following, which with the material presented in this chapter should be brought together for comparison: (1) russet scab, scab, millipede injury, and scab-gnat injury; (2) late blight and freezing injury; (3) net necrosis, frost necrosis, and stem-end discoloration; (4) grub injury and slug injury; (5) sunburn and sunscald; (6) misshape and second growth.

REFERENCES

Folsom, Donald, W. C. Libby, G. W. Simpson, and O. L. Wyman. Net necrosis of the potato. Maine Extension Bul. 246, 1938.

Hardenburg, E. V. A rare abnormality in stored potato tubers. Amer. Soc. Hort. Sci. Proc. 38, 1940.

Hardenburg, E. V., and C. N. Turner. Potato digger adjustment in relation to tuber bruising. Amer. Potato Jour. 17, No. 8, 1940.

Hastings, R. C. Grade defects of potatoes. North Dakota State Seed Dept. Bul. 21, 1932.

Jones, L. R., M. Miller, and E. Bailey. Frost necrosis of potato tubers. Wisc. Research Bul. 46, 1919.

Knorr, L. C. Ring rot of potatoes. Cornell Ext. Bul. 620, 1943.

Larson, R. H., and A. R. Albert. Physiological internal necrosis of potato tubers in Wisconsin. Jour. Agr. Research 71, No. 11, 1945.

Ross, A. Frank. Potatoes: Stem-end browning. Maine Agr. Exp. Sta. Bul. 438, 1945.

Schrumpf, William E. The effect of handling methods on quality of Maine potatoes. Maine Agr. Exp. Sta. Bul. 365, 1933.

Weiss, Freeman, and Philip Brierley. The occurrence of sprout tubers and some factors relating to their development. Potato Assn. Amer. Proc., 1926.

Werner, H. O. Hollow heart of potatoes: Occurrence and test of thiourea seed treatments for prevention. Potato Assn. Amer. Proc., 1927.

Werner, H. O. The cause and prevention of mechanical injuries to potatoes. Nebr. Agr. Exp. Sta. Bul. 260, 1931.

CHAPTER 12

Harvesting

BECAUSE of the large amount of labor and equipment required to dig, pick up, and haul potatoes, harvesting is one of the most expensive items in production. The industry was definitely limited in scope until equipment was developed to substitute for hand digging. Until a special type of shovel plow was introduced about 1882 on Long Island, the average acreage of potatoes per farm there was less than 5. The average acreage on Long Island is now over 50, and cost per bushel of harvesting has been greatly reduced with the development of tractor-hauled, two-row diggers and combines which dig, pick up, and load the crop. The trend throughout the country toward larger acreages on fewer farms and on level, well-adapted fields has made it possible to operate larger, more complicated machinery.

Date of Harvest

Potatoes are harvested almost every month of the year in some state or region. Harvest begins in southern Florida, southern Texas, and southern California and extends seasonally northward until it is ended by freezing weather in Aroostook County, Maine. This distributes the peak load for seasonal harvest labor and facilitates orderly storage and marketing. Because of its size and variation in climate, California, now the second largest potato producing state, harvests potatoes in nearly every month of the year. When weather interferes with the normal harvest schedule, competition in the market is often a problem for the early and intermediate potato states.

In order to take advantage of more favorable market prices, much of the crop grown south of the northern late states is harvested before it is mature. This involves loss of potential yield, some sacrifice in both market and culinary quality, and sometimes creates a problem of storage. Yield increases rapidly right up to the time the plant matures. This is illustrated by data reported by Campbell (1948) and adapted for use in table 49. In that table it is shown that total yield increased at least 25 per cent after one-half of the leaves on the plant were dead. The grower who harvests before maturity should weigh the sacrifice in yield against the gain in returns from harvesting early.

TABLE 49. RELATION OF TIME OF HARVEST TO YIELD OF POTA-TOES (AVERAGE OF THREE NEW JERSEY FARMS IN 1947, KATAHDIN VARIETY).

Date Harvested	Per Cent of Leaves Dead	Total Yield per Acre (100-lb. Bags)	Per Cent No. 1	Yield Increase in One Week (Per Cent)
July 22	27	229	89	—
July 29	38	268	92	17
Aug. 5	51	296	93	10
Aug. 12	55	336	94	14
Aug. 19	74	358	95	7
Aug. 26	86	362	95	1

Harvesting before maturity also usually means a sacrifice of market quality. Immature tubers are much more subject to skinning and bruising than are mature ones. Early-harvested southern pota-toes seen in northern markets during the spring and summer months are often so badly skinned or "feathered" as to appear unsightly. Such potatoes harvested and handled when the temperature is near 90° F. are likely to scald, to turn black or brown, and even to develop brown rot and other forms of bacterial decay. In extremely warm weather, immature potatoes should be harvested late in the afternoon and left in the field until morning. This procedure will permit the skin to dry and set and the tubers to cool, and will in large measure prevent sunscald and heat injury. As mentioned in a previous chapter, where the crop is infested with wireworms, millipedes and scab gnats, harvesting early is a means of reducing injury by these pests. Date of harvest is known to influence cooking quality and food values. Late-harvested or mature potatoes contain more starch and protein than those harvested when immature, because those components increase steadily as the tubers develop. Also, as will be discussed in a later chapter, the tendency for boiled peeled potatoes to turn dark after cooking is more marked when the crop matures late than early. This darkening is associated with maturity during cloudy days and low fall temperatures.

Some growers make the mistake of hastening to harvest a blight-infested crop to prevent rot of the tubers. Usually the result is disastrous in that the subsequent rot in storage is serious as a result

Fig. 103. Killing potato vines before harvest. *Left:* sprayed 10 days previously with chemical. *Right:* untreated.

of infection of sound tubers by contact with infested foliage in the harvesting process. The late blight organism, *Phytophthora infestans,* is not a saprophyte, and once the infected foliage is dead the organism can no longer contaminate the tubers. If it seems necessary to harvest a blighted field before maturity, it is best to kill or remove the tops in advance. This fact was well demonstrated by Bonde and Schultz (1945) in Maine as indicated in table 50.

Date of harvest in relation to maturity markedly influences storability or keeping quality of the crop. Bruising and skinning at time of harvest, particularly of immature potatoes, are likely to result subsequently in added loss of weight from both shrinkage and decay in storage. Newly harvested tubers are thin-skinned and

TABLE 50. RELATION OF TIME OF HARVEST OF BLIGHTED POTA-
TOES TO SUBSEQUENT ROT IN STORAGE.*

Time of Harvest	Per Cent of Tubers Showing Rot after 8 Weeks in Storage		
	1942	1943	1944
Before foliage was completely dead	20	48	53
After foliage had been killed by frost	0	4	6
Foliage partly green	—	40.0	53.0
2 days after tops killed by herbicide	—	11.0	13.6
10 days after tops killed by herbicide	—	3.0	3.0
After tops killed by frost	—	5.9	00.0

 * Adapted from Bonde and Schultz, Maine.

lose moisture faster then than at any later period. Differences in
storage weight loss between mature and immature potatoes after
7 months may be as much as 6 per cent and between carefully and
normally handled potatoes as much as 7 per cent. These differences
are shown in comparisons made in New York by Hardenburg and
Smith (1942) in table 51.

TABLE 51. EFFECT OF MANNER OF HARVESTING AND HANDLING
POTATOES ON LOSSES IN STORAGE.

Treatment	Total Weight Loss from Shrinkage and Decay	
	1 month	7 months
Immature tubers:	Per Cent	Per Cent
Carefully handled	3.05	8.07
Normally handled	5.04	11.70
Mature tubers:		
Carefully handled	2.08	5.49
Normally handled	3.78	8.45

Premature Killing of Foliage

In spite of the disadvantages of harvesting potatoes before maturity, there are several apparently good reasons for doing so. Growers of large acreages cannot risk the danger of freezing temperatures

by waiting until frost has killed the plants. The insecticide DDT apparently prolongs the period of growth beyond that safe to begin harvest. Where late blight infests the fields, the advantage of eliminating the green foliage is obvious. Recently there has been a greatly increased interest in means of quickly and cheaply killing potato plants so that harvest can begin without the inconvenience of having green foliage clog the digger and obscure tubers on the ground, and without exposing the tubers to skinning and bruising.

Fig. 104. Killing potato vines with a flame thrower.

The benefits of vine killing are somewhat dependent on the timeliness of the operation. At least a few days should intervene between killing and harvest to allow the skin on the tubers to set and the tops to die. Those methods which are slow in action, notably some of the chemical treatments, seem to reduce yield less but require earlier application than do those methods which kill quickly. Most of the chemical vine killers are preferably applied about a week before harvest, even though this may mean considerable sacrifice of yield. Some large growers have been known to sacrifice as much as 100 bushels to the acre because of the necessity of beginning the harvest on time.

There are at present three principal methods of killing potato vines: by chemical spray or dust, by burning with flame throwing equipment, and by mechanical beaters. Until their use has passed the experimental stage, it will be difficult to know which method is the most efficient and the most economical. The two types of chemical defoliants most used in spray form are dinitros, either with or without activators, and arsenicals. The latter are perhaps more dangerous to handle, and it is not definitely known whether ab-

Fig. 105. The rotobeater kills vines mechanically and leaves organic matter in soil.

sorbed arsenic may eventually be a health hazard. Since these chemicals are somewhat corrosive, the sprayer should be thoroughly rinsed after using. Although the regular Bordeaux sprayer can be used, costs can be lowered by using special nozzle equipment to reduce the gallonage required for adequate coverage. The materials are more quickly effective if applied during hot, dry weather. A third chemical is cyanamid, sold as aero-defoliant and applied as a dust. It is relatively cheap but should be applied only when the plants are wet.

The second means developed for killing vines was the flame thrower or weed burner. This is a specially designed machine which burns petroleum and applies a flame under pressure to two rows at a time. Usually a second application is necessary for a complete

Fig. 106. Plow used for digging potatoes in some southern states.

Fig. 107. Covering barrels of immature Cobblers in Virginia to prevent scald and for later shipment.

kill, although completeness of kill depends on rate of drive through the field. This method is relatively expensive and dangerous.

The latest development is the mechanical beater or vine shredder which beats the plant into small particles and leaves it on the ground. The device is essentially a cylinder carrying many rubber flails and revolving at about 700 r.p.m. It presents the advantages of a quick disposal of the foliage, with virtually no trash left to cover the tubers and with no loss of organic matter (as there is in the case of the chemical sprays and the burner). The flame thrower and a roto-beater are shown in figures 104 and 105.

The importance of saving potato tops as a source of organic matter should not be underestimated. Naturally, the amount varies with the size of plant characteristic of each variety. It may range from about ½ ton for early, small-growing varieties, such as Cobbler, to 1½ tons of air-dry organic matter to the acre for prolific foliage varieties, such as Sequoia. This variation is illustrated by data procured by the author and shown in table 52.

TABLE 52. AIR-DRY WEIGHT OF POTATO TOPS BASED ON SAMPLES HARVESTED AT ITHACA, N.Y., OCT. 7, 1947 (NET WEIGHT OF 25 PLANTS FROM 25 FEET OF ROW).

Variety	October 7	November 4	Air-dry Weight on Nov. 4 (Pounds per Acre)
	Uncured Sample (Pounds)	Cured Sample (Pounds)	
Cobbler	2.00	2.00	1162
Katahdin	4.00	2.25	1307
Placid	5.75	3.00	1742
Rural	4.25	3.00	1742
Green Mountain	8.50	4.75	2759
Sequoia	14.50	5.75	3340
Average	6.50	3.46	2009

Digging Equipment and Methods

Hand digging of potatoes is no longer appropriate or practical except in the home garden and on areas not exceeding one or two acres. Field studies have shown that hand digging results in more mechanical injury to the crop than does machine digging. Injury done in hand digging is of course done by either fork or hook tines. Early in the twentieth century, machine diggers were developed to lessen the onus of harvest. The objectives were to get the tubers out of the soil, separate them, and leave them on the ground for picking. Very little, if any, thought was given to protection against mechanical injury. Three principal types of diggers are now in general use, the oldest or shaker-bar type, the extension apron or double-apron type, and the continuous or single-apron type. Increasingly the trend is toward the single apron model and toward a leveling of the digger bed. This change is aimed at a reduction of bruising of the tubers. A modern, two-row, level bed type of digger is shown in figure 108. More recently, combines or machines which dig, pick up, and sack potatoes all in one operation have come into

Fig. 108. Digging with 2-row, continuous apron digger. Note rubber tires and outside rear-drive chain.

fairly general use on Long Island and in other regions where the fields are large, level, and free from stones. These machines are not yet adapted to sloping fields and to places where the soil is cluttered with stones and clods. The average life of a potato digger varies from 5 to 10 years depending on the acreage dug annually and the care given it.

The type of digger and the manner in which it is equipped and operated greatly influence the amount of mechanical injury to the crop. Field studies in Maine, Nebraska, and New York show that from 10 to 40 per cent of the tubers are bruised in the digging process. More than one-half of all damage found in potatoes in retail stores in our large cities consists of old cuts and bruises. For this the digger appears to be the principal offender. Hardenburg and Turner (1940) made a comparison of 61 diggers on 32 New York farms in respect to relation of type of digger to amount of bruising. They found the most injury being done by the double-apron type, next most by the old shaker-bar digger, and least by the newer single-apron type. Their study demonstrated that bruising by the digger can be appreciably reduced by: (1) setting the point deep enough to carry dirt at least two-thirds back on the chain, (2) reducing the speed of the chain to about 7 r.p.m., (3) reduction of agitation by removal of most of the jump sprockets under the chain

Fig. 109. Using crates to pick up and haul a 400-bushel crop of immature Sebago variety on the farm of Bruce Cottrell, Homer, N.Y.

and replacing with rollers, (4) tightening the chain by removal of rods to eliminate whip, and (5) removal or padding of the rear tine guards. On most farms there is now sufficient tractor power so that there is very little excuse not to carry enough soil to cushion the tubers over the digger chain. The elimination of digger bruises is more a matter of care and method of operation on the part of the operator than of type of digger.

Where average yields are high, picking of the tubers is one of the most costly items. Equipment is being developed to convey the tubers directly from the digger onto a picking table trailed behind or mounted with the digger into a so-called combine. This equipment either sacks the potatoes or conveys them into bulk-loaded trucks driven alongside. Walker and Mumford (1944) of Oregon have made careful estimates of the size of labor crews needed to harvest 4 acres per day and yields of 250 to 300 hundred-pound sacks per acre with different methods and equipment. To harvest and store such a crop, including hauling as far as ¾ mile and using one-row equipment, their estimates of size of crews were as follows:

Fig. 110. The use of baskets and barrels to harvest the potato crop is customary in Maine.

Fig. 111. A single-row combine equipped to dig, grade, and sack potatoes on Long Island.

Digger, 12 pickers, 21; Digger and trailer-sacker, 14; Combine digger-sacker, 14; Combine digger-bulker, 10. These figures indicate that by eliminating hand picking, the labor requirement can be reduced by one-third to one-half.

In the South where hand labor is comparatively cheap and most of the crop is harvested immature, a simple type of mule-drawn, turn-plow is used to dig the crop. This at least has the advantages of less bruising. Also the tubers are picked up closely behind the plow to avoid sunscald.

Picking and Handling Equipment

Much of the commercial crop is still picked by hand. Fast pickers, often women and children, are nimble-fingered, and, if yield is high and trash and tops are not troublesome, can pick up as many as 100

Fig. 112. Half-bushel, rigid-handled, woven-splint baskets are efficient and bruise very few potatoes.

to 150 bushels a day. In western Nebraska and in Idaho, a picking belt is used; to that a burlap sack is snapped and trailed between the picker's legs (see figure 113). When the sack is about half full, it is unsnapped and replaced by an empty one. This is satisfactory where there are no stones on the ground to bruise the potatoes. On Long Island, in New Jersey, in the South, in California, and in Maine splint baskets are used, and, as these are filled, the potatoes are poured into sacks for loading and hauling (figure 112). Picking and hauling to storage in bushel slatted crates is the method still generally used in upstate New York and Pennsylvania. In Maine most of the crop is picked in baskets and dumped into barrels for hauling to storage. According to Schrumpf (1933), most of the bruises found in Maine potatoes is the result of digging and placing in storage. According to his study a total of 7.1 per cent of major in-juries resulted from dig-ging and storage, of which 1.75 per cent were due to digging, 1.94 per cent to emptying into barrels, and 2.65 per cent to placing in storage. The various steps in grading later added a total of 7.3 per cent of major bruises. In most of the potato areas of Cali-fornia, the procedure is to pick into half sacks, load onto trucks, haul to the packing shed, empty onto conveyor, wash, sort, sack, and load into railroad cars.

Picking containers vary considerably in their effect on the amount of bruising. Hardenburg (1938) com-pared crates, splint baskets,

Fig. 113. A canvas belt to which the sack being used is suspended, and empty sacks hooked on the picker's back are used in Idaho and Nebraska.

wire baskets, and tin pails used in picking potatoes on 105 New York farms. Crates resulted in the most bruising, 2.25 per cent, and splint baskets the least, 1.57 per cent. Where yields are low and it is necessary to carry a nearly filled crate, pickers are tempted to throw potatoes some distance. This results in much bruising of the potatoes against the slats. A ¾-bushel padded basket is probably least offensive in this respect.

Fig. 114. Motor-driven barrel hoist is convenient for loading barrels. (Clark Seed Farms, Richford, N.Y.)

REFERENCES

Bonde, Reiner, and E. S. Schultz. Potatoes. Effect of time of digging on late-blight rot in storage. Maine Agr. Exp. Sta. Bul. 438, 1945.

Campbell, John C. Weekly potato yield increases—1947. New Jersey Hints to Potato Growers 29, No. 3, 1948.

Hardenburg, E. V. Potato growing in New York. Cornell Ext. Bul. 239, 1938.

Hardenburg, E. V., and Ora Smith. Harvesting and storing potatoes. Cornell Ext. Bul. 532, 1942.

Hardenburg, E. V., and C. N. Turner. Potato digger adjustment in relation to tuber bruising. Amer. Potato Jour. 17, No. 8, 1940.

Schrumpf, William E. The effect of handling methods on quality of Maine potatoes. Maine Agr. Exp. Sta. Bul. 365, 1933.

Walker, Clyde, and D. Curtis Mumford. Potato harvesting methods in Oregon. Ore. Agr. Exp. Sta. Circ. of Infor. 345, 1944.

CHAPTER 13

Storage

THE STORAGE of potatoes on farms in the surplus-producing late potato states of the north is general practice. In California and in the Gulf and South Atlantic states almost none of the crop is stored on farms where it is produced.

Functions

The functions of potato storage are mainly economic and practical. From the economic standpoint, storage helps to stabilize prices by avoiding glutted markets and helps to equalize labor distribution on farms where marketing might otherwise compete seriously with harvest operations. Practically, storage is a means of preserving potatoes in their best physical condition and culinary quality and of protecting them against the hazards of excessively high and low temperatures. According to data collected by the Bureau of Agricultural Economics of the United States Department of Agriculture, about 25 to 30 per cent of the total merchantable stocks produced in the thirty-five late-potato states is still on hand as late as January 1. Of this total, an average of more than 80 per cent is stored on farms where grown. Since the potato is about 80 per cent water, it is comparatively perishable, and its proper storage requires some knowledge of its physiology.

Essentials of Good Storage

Attention to several fundamentals is essential if the potato crop is to be stored successfully. The tubers should be clean, mature, and free from injury. Dirty tubers favor the invasion of rot-producing organisms and interfere with the circulation of air throughout the storage bin. Immature potatoes are more subject to shrinkage from excess water loss than are mature potatoes. Mechanically injured and diseased tubers are likely to rot unless temperature and humidity are so regulated as to prevent it.

Temperature should be so regulated as to protect against freezing, provide a minimum of fluctuation, and preferably a range of 36° to 40° F. to prevent sprouting. Humidity should range near 90 per cent of saturation so that the stored crop will lose a minimum of weight from moisture evaporation and transpiration; it should be so well controlled as not to condense on the ceiling and other wooden parts of the room, causing them to rot, and yet to be retained within the storage at all times.

The insulation of potato storage should be such as to protect the potatoes against freezing, maintain a uniform temperature, and protect structural materials against decay from condensation of moisture in the wrong places. Since potatoes respire in storage, enough ventilation should be available to provide oxygen, eliminate carbon dioxide and heat of respiration, and control humidity. However, only a minimum of ventilation is needed usually, because there is enough leakage through doors and windows to provide an occasional change of air. Finally it is important that stored potatoes be kept in total darkness to prevent greening.

Temperature Relations

Of all the factors enumerated under essentials, temperature is the most important. It influences the rate at which the life processes in the stored tuber progress, especially respiration, carbohydrate changes, breakage of the rest period, and duration of dormancy. The tendency of all these processes is to accelerate as temperature increases. According to Wright (1932): "The general rule of Van't Hoff (that the respiration rate doubles or trebles for each 10° C. [18° F.] rise in temperature) does not hold for low temperatures." Instead a greater rate of respiration is generally found at 36° F. than at 32° or 40°. Kimbrough (1925) and Smith (1933) showed that the respiration rate is most rapid immediately following harvest, again after any sudden change from a low to a higher temperature, and finally when sprouting begins late in the storage period. As had been pointed out previously by Bushnell, Hartman, Smith, and other workers, the usual effect of increasingly higher temperatures in storage of seed is to increase rate of emergence of plants and increase sprout number per seed piece. It is now well known that stored tubers sprout readily at any temperature above 40° F. This, therefore, is the threshold or sprouting temperature, and a good storage for potatoes to be held more than 4 months should constantly maintain a temperature below this level.

Culinary quality and carbohydrate content are greatly influenced by temperature. Tubers stored below 40° F. are likely to develop a sweetish taste because of a reduced rate of respiration and the consequent accumulation of sugars. Regardless of temperature, the normal carbohydrate changes involve the hydrolysis of starch to

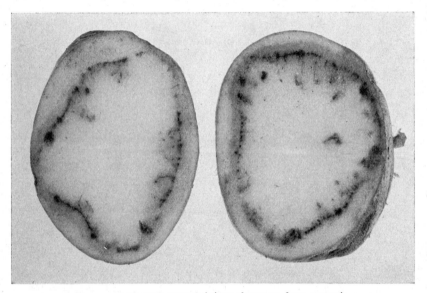

Fig. 115. Low-temperature injury shown as frost necrosis.

sugar and the breakdown of sugar into carbon dioxide and water as products of respiration. Within the temperature range of 40° to 80° F., sugars are used as rapidly as formed. However, when the temperature range is below 40° F., respiration is retarded and sugar accumulates. This accumulation appears to be about equally true for both sucrose and reducing sugars, and the result is not only a sweetish taste but a darker-colored cooked product. Storing the raw product for a period of 10 days to 2 weeks at higher temperatures results in a higher rate of respiration and dissipation of the accumulated sugar. Wright *et al.* (1936) compared the cooking quality of four varieties previously stored at 32°, 36°, 40°, 50°, and 60° F. The result was that tubers stored at the higher temperatures had a superior texture (mealiness), color, and flavor when cooked.

Freezing or low-temperature injury to potato tubers is a phase which should be better understood by both growers and handlers. Potatoes do not ordinarily freeze until the temperature approximates 29° F. Frost injury is a term used to designate damage caused by freezing temperatures before the crop is harvested. Freezing injury is damage occurring when potatoes are in storage or in transit. Actual damage is the result of cell rupture caused by the formation of ice crystals. Wright and Diehl (1927) showed that the actual freezing point of any lot of potatoes varies with the temperature at which it has been previously stored. They also showed that disturbance of potatoes exposed to a temperature below freezing may greatly increase the resulting damage. Averages for three varieties previously stored for 15 weeks at 32°, 40°, and 50° F., obtained by these workers, are shown in table 53.

TABLE 53. RELATION OF STORAGE TEMPERATURE TO FREEZING POINT AND OF DISTURBANCE TO FREEZING DAMAGE.

Previous Storage Temperature in Degrees F.	Freezing Point on March 16 in Degrees F.	Per Cent of Potatoes Injured When Exposed to 20.5° F.	
		Undisturbed	Disturbed
32	28.6	0.0	51.7
40	29.7	0.0	66.7
50	30.0	26.7	90.0

In table 53 are figures indicating that stored potatoes will not freeze so quickly when they have been stored at a low temperature as when they have been stored at a higher temperature. This can be explained on the basis of their higher sugar content. It is also evident that any movement or disturbance of potatoes undercooled or exposed to temperatures below their actual freezing point may greatly increase the amount of damage. This phenomenon has been termed freezing inoculation, a process whereby ice-crystal formation is initiated. It indicates that potatoes subject to freezing temperatures before harvest, while in transit or in storage, should not be harvested or handled until the tubers have thawed or until all danger of further damage is past. Symptoms of low-temperature injury are of many types, varying from slight darkening of the vascular ring through necrosis and blotching of the parenchyma tissue to complete breakdown of the tuber. Frost necrosis of the net type is difficult to distinguish from net necrosis caused by the leaf roll virus.

According to Folsom and Goven (1947), storage temperature influences the development of net necrosis and of stem-end browning in the tuber. In their studies, the higher the temperature above 32° F., the greater the percentage of net necrosis tubers of cull

Fig. 116. Pit or outdoor pile storage used temporarily on Long Island.

grade. With stem-end browning "exposure at the lower temperatures tended to prevent permanently any further development of the symptoms after shifting of the samples to 50° F." Relatively high storage temperature, especially where potatoes are stored in an atmosphere of limited oxygen supply, sometimes causes a physiological breakdown called blackheart. This is most likely to occur in winter carlot shipments where heaters are used to prevent freezing in transit. The higher temperature exhausts the supply of oxygen necessary for normal respiration. Bennett and Bartholomew (1924) illustrate the usual symptom of a black decay, mainly of the inner medulla, and explain that it is due to a deficit of oxygen rather than to an accumulation of carbon dioxide. In their control experiments, they state that "the available supply of oxygen diffusing inward from the surface of the tuber was used up before it reached the interior tissues which died as a result of asphyxiation."

Although very little of the table stock grown in the South is stored, there is considerable interest in the storage of seed. For planting the main crop which is harvested in the spring, northern-grown certified seed is usually placed in common storage. The difficulty with using southern, fall-grown seed for the spring crop is that it is slower to germinate than northern-grown seed. To remedy this difficulty, Kimbrough (1944) recommended that the southern-grown seed, often referred to as second-crop seed, be stored at temperatures as high as 80° F. to shorten the rest period and induce earlier sprouting. With such treatment, the results from northern- and southern-grown seed are said to be about equal.

Fig. 117. Trackside potato storage in Vermont.

Humidity Requirements

Since stored potato tubers contain nearly 80 per cent of water, they are subject to shrinkage from water loss in storage. The relative humidity of a good storage, therefore, should be maintained at 80 to 90 per cent. It should be high enough to prevent shrinkage, yet low enough to avoid condensation on any surface which might rot structural materials or cause dripping of moisture onto the tubers. The aim should be to retain all moisture within the storage to prevent shrinkage. This means that excess ventilation and the use of too many outtake flues should be avoided. To reduce humidity loss to a minimum, it may be advisable to provide a condensing surface on the coldest side of the storage so that the natural moisture given off by the tubers will condense on it, run down to the floor into a gutter, and there evaporate again into the storage air. This condensing surface should be sheet metal suspended on the inside of a driveway door or the upper unbanked portion of a concrete wall.

Types of Storage

Farm storages vary in type and size throughout the northern late potato states largely according to climatic conditions and volume of potatoes to be stored. They can be classed into six types, in the approximate order of capacity used, as bank or underground type, aboveground or special house (as on Long Island), combination above- and below-ground type (as in Maine and North Dakota), farm basement type, house celler, and pit storage.

Fig. 118. A modern 30,000-bushel bank storage in northern New York.

Bank storage offers such advantages over other types as protection against freezing injury without expensive insulation and a desirably low temperature maintained with a minimum of fluctuation. It is usually preferred to aboveground storage where a steam shovel is available for excavation, and where there is plenty of sloping ground to provide filling and banking against the side walls.

Aboveground storage requires expensive insulation and does not offer the advantage of easy filling of the bins. In Maine, Idaho, and North Dakota farm storage is mainly of the bank type, while track-side storage is principally superstructure. Wilson and Hardenburg (1931), reporting on 259 farm storages in New York, found a majority to be house cellars, but these were least satisfactory from the standpoint of shrinkage. Bank storage maintained the lowest temperature and the highest humidity and resulted in least shrinkage.

Pit or mound storage is the oldest type and cheapest to construct, but when the stored crop is unsound, dirty, or diseased, losses may be high. Also there is danger of freezing when the pit is opened during severe winter weather. Edgar (1947) reported that where the average annual temperature is above 55° F. potatoes cannot be satisfactorily stored in pits for more than 3 or 4 months. Pits are made by leveling a floor of earth 6 to 12 feet wide, and as long as required. The potatoes are piled 1 to 3 feet deep in pyramid form and covered with alternate layers of straw and earth as deep as protection from freezing requires. Covering too deeply in mild weather may induce early sprouting.

Storage Construction

In planning to build a potato storage, one should consider cost, convenience, and efficiency. Efficiency as concerned with preserving quality and condition of the tubers requires good insulation, durable construction, and ample ventilation. The advice of a qualified agricultural engineer may avoid costly mistakes difficult to remedy later. It costs no more, or very little more, to build right than to follow the advice of some grower who has had experience of the wrong kind. Expert advice is available at no cost, and building plans can be had at a nominal charge. A mistake often made is to build the storage too small. Later alterations and additions are relatively costly. In estimating the capacity desired, plenty of working space for grading, sacking, and loading should be provided. Actual storage capacity can be figured with the formula,

$$\frac{L \times W}{1.244} = \text{bushels' capacity per foot of depth, when L and W repre-}$$

sent floor length and width respectively in feet. Plans and bills of material for storages of various sizes and types have been presented by Edgar (1947). Similarly, structural advice and plans for proper air circulation, insulation, condensing area, vapor proofing, ventilation, walls, chimneys, floors, and doorways have been given by Goodman (1945). Concrete walls are preferable to cinder blocks and concrete blocks if made about 18 inches thick at the base and 12 inches thick at the top. If blocks are used, they must be braced with pilasters and properly designed to withstand ground pressure. Vapor proofing of the insulation used in ceilings and walls is essential if the insulation is to be protected against absorption of

Fig. 119. A cheap, efficient type of bank storage at Kimberly, Idaho.

moisture. Provision for the flow of air currents down the side walls and up through the piled potatoes is the best means of avoiding "hot spots" and for the preservation of tubers at the center of the piles or bins. Most of these essentials are illustrated in figure 120 as given by Goodman.

Most of the large storage houses provide for storing in deep bins with single or double slatted sides. These bin partitions provide considerable circulation of air through the piles, but they may also increase shrinkage and some loss of vitamins. Recently a new type of storage called shell-cooled storage has been designed. This system consists of circulating air under and around the bins with tight walls and floors rather than through the mass of potatoes. It is most satisfactory where power-operated blowers and thermostatic controls are used.

Storage Shrinkage

Stored potatoes lose weight by respiration, by evaporation, and by sprouting and decay. Depending on storage construction and management, condition of the tubers, and length of storage period this loss of weight varies from 2 to 8 per cent. Temperature, humidity, variety, and type of storage container are important factors in storage shrinkage. During the period November 4, 1947, to March 12, 1948, the author stored two varieties in three types of storage and in five types of 15-pound consumer packages. The average loss in weight was about 4 per cent, and there was no significant difference in loss between storage in the slatted crate and sacks made of saxolin, Chasenet, paper, cotton, and burlap. The average shrinkage for each variety in the three storages is shown in table 54.

The results of this study indicate that shrinkage tends to be highest where the humidity is lowest, and that Sebago, an early-sprouting, poor-keeping

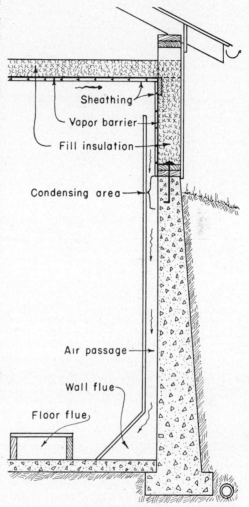

Fig. 120. Cross section showing details of concrete and wooden-wall construction for bank storage. (Agr. Engineering Dept., Cornell Univ.)

variety shrinks faster than Houma, a good keeper. Werner (1936) found that potatoes stored in sacks lost less weight during the fall and winter but more in the spring than those stored in crates.

Sprouting and decay were more pronounced in the sacks in spring because of poorer aeration. Unless special provision for aeration is made, sack storage over long periods is not recommended. In Kansas where most of the crop is not stored, but some of it is held in cold storage, Parsons (1942) compared the shrinkage of washed and un-washed potatoes. When the amount of tuber damage was small, there was no difference in shrinkage, but when damage was severe, the washed lots shrank more. Parsons also found that when stored over a 6-month period, potatoes held in open-mesh consumer sacks lost considerably more weight than did similar lots held in either burlap or close-woven cotton sacks.

TABLE 54. RELATION OF TYPE OF STORAGE TO SHRINKAGE
NOV. 4–MARCH 12.

Type of Storage	Average Temperature (Degrees F.)	Average Humidity (Per Cent)	Weight Loss in Per Cent	
			Houma	Sebago
Refrigerated	52	75	2.60	4.34
House cellar	48	35	2.77	7.90
Insulated bank	40	65	1.91	5.12

Sprout Inhibitors

In many storages, as the temperature increases toward spring, sprouting of the tubers becomes a matter of shrinkage and lowered market quality. Recently methods and materials have been de-veloped whereby such sprouting can be inhibited or delayed for several weeks. The most efficient method is to apply a sprout in-hibiting hormone, either as a spray or a dust, to the tubers as they are being placed in storage. Smith *et al.* (1947) and others have found that the methyl ester of naphthaleneacetic acid in liquid form will effectively retard sprouting in storage even at temperatures above 50° F. Applied in excess, it shows some interference with the normal healing of tuber injuries and may even cause a pitting of the tuber surface. More recently, these workers applied the above material and other sprout-inhibiting hormones as a spray to the growing plants. In excess, the effects on the plants were severe upward rolling of the leaves, a pitting of the tubers, and a lowering of both specific gravity and yield. However, at lower concentrations, sodium 2,4-D, naphthaleneacetic acid, and indoleacetic acid applied at 55 to 110 gallons to the acre did not affect plant, yield, or quality, and did effectively retard sprout growth of the stored tubers after 3 months at 50° F. It therefore appears that hormone treatment of the growing plant may become an appropriate means of solving one of the more difficult problems of potato storage.

REFERENCES

Bennett, J. P., and E. T. Bartholomew. The respiration of potato tubers in relation to the occurrence of blackheart. Univ. of Calif. Tech. Paper No. 14, 1924.

Edgar, Alfred D. Potato storage. U.S. Dept. Agr. Farmers' Bul. 1986, 1947.

Folsom, Donald, and Michael Goven. Potatoes: Net necrosis and stem-end browning in storage at different temperatures. Maine Agr. Exp. Sta. Bul. 449, 1947.

Goodman, A. M. Farm potato storages and their management. Cornell Extension Bul. 615, rev. 1945.

Kimbrough, William Duke. A study of respiration in potatoes with special reference to storage and transpiration. Md. Agr. Exp. Sta. Bul. 276, 1925.

Kimbrough, W. D. Storage of Irish potatoes in the lower south. La. Agr. Exp. Sta. Bul. 386, 1944.

Parsons, Franklin L. Some cold-storage studies of Kansas potatoes. Kans. Agr. Exp. Sta. Bul. 310, 1942.

Smith, Ora. Studies of potato storage. Cornell Univ. Agr. Exp. Sta. Bul. 553, 1933.

Smith, Ora, M. A. Baeza, and J. H. Ellison. Response of potato plants to spray applications of certain growth-regulating substances. Bot. Gaz. 108, No. 3, 1947.

Werner, H. O. Cellar and cold storage of sound and of mechanically damaged Triumph seed potatoes. Nebr. Agr. Exp. Sta. Research Bul. 88, 1936.

Wilson, A. L., and E. V. Hardenburg. Potato storage on 259 farms in New York. Cornell Univ. Agr. Exp. Sta. Bul. 526, 1931.

Wright, R. C., and H. C. Diehl. Freezing injury to potatoes. U.S. Dept Agr. Tech. Bul. 27, 1927.

Wright, R. C. Some physiological studies of potatoes in storage. Jour. Agr. Research 45, No. 9, 1932.

Wright, R. C., Walter M. Peacock, T. M. Whiteman, and Elizabeth Fuller Whiteman. The cooking quality, palatability, and carbohydrate composition of potatoes as influenced by storage temperature. U.S. Dept. Agr. Tech. Bul. 507, 1936.

CHAPTER 14

Grading and Marketing

F IELD-RUN POTATOES, like other food commodities, vary in size and the number of defective specimens harvested. Because of this variation, they need a certain amount of sorting, grading, sizing, or other form of standardization to make them attractive to the buyer.

Necessity of grading

Formerly, when it was universally possible to sell potatoes subject to the personal inspection of the buyer, ungraded potatoes could be merchandised according to mutual agreement. With our present system of long-distance bargaining, fair pricing is possible only when the product is so well standardized that both buyer and seller have the same understanding of market quality. To standardize a product so that it can be quoted in the market requires the promulgation of official grade standards which can be known and recognized universally. Such grade standards for potatoes were developed by the United States Department of Agriculture and have been in use, although frequently revised, since 1917. The several functions of grade standards were well outlined by Spangler (1946) when he said: "They furnish the yardstick for measuring variations in quality, and their use has made possible a basis for satisfactory long-distance dealing." More specifically they (1) make possible a market news and a price reporting service, (2) provide a basis for settling disputes between buyers and sellers, (3) facilitate the issuance of crop loans, (4) furnish a basis for advertising, and (5) make it possible for the members of growers' co-operative organizations to pool their returns.

To many growers, grading means merely sizing with very little concern about the removal of defective tubers. Overloading the grading table, poor lighting, and carelessness are responsible for much of the dissatisfaction with the quality of market potatoes. However, the most careful grading possible will not make a fancy pack out of poor field-run stock. Most potatoes are not good enough to warrant an attempt to pack U.S. Fancy grade, and many lots are too dirty or too badly damaged to make it advisable to grade them better than U.S. Commercial. For these reasons the potatoes to be graded should first be carefully appraised.

Fig. 121. A quality product, well graded and attractively packed, is essential to successful marketing. (Vegetable Crops Dept., Cornell Univ.)

It would be unwise to say that all potatoes should be graded before being sold. Sometimes it is mutually satisfactory to grower and buyer to handle the crop field-run. If the potatoes are sold on a graded basis, it is usually cheaper and more satisfactory in the long run to do the grading at the farm or at some central grading point. When the crop is to be stored at the farm, it is better not to grade it until time to market. If the potatoes are dirty and carry more or less soft rot, it may be advisable to screen them before storage so that they will store better. Otherwise, putting them over the grader merely adds to the skinning, bruising and shrinkage and does not eliminate the need for grading later.

Grade Standards

The official standards for grading potatoes as promulgated by the United States Department of Agriculture are published in Service and Regulatory Announcements No. 151 (1942). These grades have been officially adopted by the several states and are in general use. Their use is not compulsory, and in most states potatoes are not required to be sold on a graded basis. However, under the federal misbranding law, it is a misdemeanor to sell or expose for sale potatoes in closed packages under a grade designation with which the contents of the package do not comply.

Grade standards are sometimes criticized as being too complicated to be practical and readily understood. Nevertheless, if standards are to be useful, they must clearly delimit and describe the tubers permissible in each grade. To qualify as an efficient grader of potatoes, one does not need to be able to diagnose the cause of the defect or damage. It is necessary, however, to know and observe the requirements as to size, defects, and tolerances for each of the four specified standard grades. The principal grade is U.S. No. 1, the minimum size of which is 1⅞ inches. There is no maximum size limit for any grade except as one wishes so to specify in the brand. To simplify the definition of the four standard grades as to size, defects, and tolerance for each, the following schedule has been prepared.

U.S. Grade Standards for Potatoes

Grade	Size	Defects
(1) U.S. Fancy	2 inches minimum. Long var: not less than 40% 6 oz. or over in weight. Short var: not less than 60% 2¼ inches or larger.	Firm, bright, well-shaped. Free from *injury*.* Tolerance = not more than 6% below requirements.
(2) U.S. No. 1	1⅞ inches minimum. Tolerance = not more	Free from *damage*.† Tolerance = not more

* Injury: Loss of more than 2 per cent but less than 5 per cent of gross weight of tuber, including peeling, in preparation for the table.

† Damage: Loss of more than 5 per cent but less than 10 per cent of gross weight of tuber, including peeling, in preparation for the table.

Grade	Size	Defects
	than 3% below minimum size.	than 6% below requirements.
(3) U.S. Commercial	1⅞ inches minimum. Tolerance = not more than 3% below minimum size.	Free from *damage* † except dirt. Tolerance = not more than 20% below requirements.
(4) U.S. No. 2	1½ inches minimum. Tolerance = not more than 3% below minimum size.	Free from *serious damage.*‡ Tolerance not = more than 6% below requirements.

Variety	Size A	Size B
(5) Russet Burbank, Netted Gem, White Rose, and other long varieties.	Minimum 1⅞ inches. Not less than 40% 6 oz. or larger.	1½ to 2 inches.
(6) Cobbler, Triumph, Green Mountain, Katahdin, Rurals, Sebago, Red McClure, and other round varieties.	Minimum 1⅞ inches. Not less than 60% 2¼ inches, or larger.	1½ to 2 inches.

‡ Serious damage: Loss of more than 10 per cent of gross weight of tuber, including peeling, in preparation for the table.

The purpose of the tolerances specified is to allow for error in grading even when the most careful attempt at accuracy is made. Deliberately to leave undersized or damaged tubers in the graded lot is almost certain to result in rejection on inspection. In determining whether No. 1 potatoes are in grade, federal-state inspectors usually combine the weights of damaged and seriously damaged tubers to calculate whether the tolerance has been exceeded.

Grading Equipment

Equipment for processing potatoes includes such items as screening tables for the removal of dirt, sizing belts, brushers, washers, sorting tables, driers, bagging machines, and conveyors for loading.

Small-scale operators commonly use a hand grader which screens out dirt and very small tubers, and sizes No. 1 and No. 2 size potatoes. More extensive operations make use of power-driven sizing units attached to canvas belts or roller tables for the removal of damaged tubers and trash. Rollers give the advantage of rotating the tubers so that, with good light, defects on both sides of the tuber can be

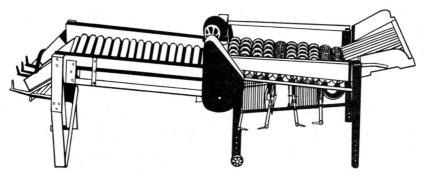

Fig. 122. Good grading equipment provides screens for sizing and a picking table for sorting. (John Bean Mfg. Co.)

seen. Without proper care, considerable mechanical injury may be added, especially to immature, newly harvested, or brittle tubers. Thoroughness of the job of grading requires good light, proper speed of operation, and care not to overload the grader.

Brushing and Washing

Since eye appeal is one of the most important factors influencing consumer preference in the market, the removal of dirt by brushing or washing is important. Mature, sound, fairly clean potatoes harvested from sandy loam soils may not warrant the extra cost of cleaning. The crop from sticky soil or muck and peat soils will usually bring some premium if brushed or washed. Since about 1935, washing has become more and more general practice in the South and in the West especially for the early crop and for long-distance shipment. Scarcely any potatoes are washed in the East and near large consuming centers. The premium price for washed potatoes from any locality has varied from 5 to 25 cents the 100-pound sack. The cost of washing has averaged about 5 cents per hundred-weight.

Brushing is done by passing the tubers over a series of rollers covered with fiber bristles and under cloth flaps. Washers are more complicated and more expensive; they are of various types. Vincent and Garver (1936) describe three types of washers in use in Washington. These are the spray type, the flood or splash type, and the abrasive type. The capacity of these machines varied from 1 to 5 tons per hour and the power requirements from 1½ to 5 horsepower. The quantity of water required varied according to the system used but averaged about 1,000 gallons per ton of potatoes. Using cold water, the precooling effect resulted in less shrinkage

Fig. 123. For grading in the field, a hand shaker type hauled through the field at Greeley, Colorado.

and better keeping in transit. Barger *et al*. (1942) precooled potatoes shipped from Kern County, California, by a shower in water at 35° F. This hydrocooled the tubers from 80° F. to 50° F. in 15 minutes and resulted in eliminating the tendency of the skinned areas to blacken; they arrived at destination in almost perfect condition. Ramsey *et al*. (1944) compared various methods of precooling of washed early potatoes shipped from central Nebraska and from Colorado to Chicago. The ordinary or standard ventilation of potatoes shipped in 100-pound sacks in warm weather was not satisfactory because it did not prevent scalding, rotting, blackening, and shriveling in transit. Preicing of cars before loading was the most economically satisfactory method and did not prevent wound healing. Preicing and reicing in transit gave excellent refrigeration but the potatoes arrived so cold that moisture condensed on them several hours after unloading. Poole and Barr (1941) found that an efficient bunker-fan unit was very satisfactory for precooling Louisiana washed potatoes while they were being loaded. They state that it is not advisable to have a potato temperature below 55° F. when shipping under standard ventilation.

Packing and Packaging

Convenience and cleanliness are increasingly demanded by retail food buyers. Although the retail sale of potatoes from bulk lots affords the buyer the opportunity to inspect and choose, it is neither

Fig. 124. A power-driven, bagging machine with capacity for 2000 10-pound sacks per hour.

clean nor convenient, and it usually results in more waste and shrinkage to be absorbed in the seller's costs. Potatoes are increasingly being marketed in small consumer-size packages, the most popular being the 15-pound paper sack. The sack usually carries a brand name, the name and address of the packer, the grade designation, and, according to law, the net weight of the contents. The 100-pound burlap sack is still the most common package, next is the 15-pound paper sack, while a few potatoes are packaged in 10- and 5-pound bags. In a few states, potatoes are sold in 50- and 60-pound bags. Cost of packing is more or less inversely related to size of package. Open-mesh or the net type of container is less popular than paper or cotton cloth because it allows dirt to sift out and the tubers to become greened when exposed to light.

Federal-State Inspection

In all of the states, since provision was made by Congress for it in 1922, an official inspection service has been available at both shipping points and in terminal markets. Under a contract agreement between the federal government and some official state agency in each state, trained inspectors can be called in to determine and report on such factors as grade, method of loading, type of package, quality and condition of the product. The service is available at nominal cost in more than fifty of the larger cities and at many shipping points during the season when potatoes are being shipped or transported in large volume. For many years the cost to the applicant was $4.00 the carload for the initial inspection and more for reinspection. If inspection required considerable travel expense for the inspector, an additional fee was levied to cover this item.

Regional supervisors are usually in charge of the hiring, training, licensing, and allocation of inspectors. Monies collected for inspection service are turned into a revolving fund administered by the state agency, usually the state department of agriculture. This makes the service largely self-supporting and not a liability on public taxes.

Benefits from the inspection service are commensurate with the needs for it. On a rising or a stable market, there is less need for the service than on a market where prices are falling.

Freezing or overheating in transit are sometimes the source of controversy between shipper and receiver. Potatoes shipped in good condition may arrive out of grade and be rejected at the terminal market. Claims for losses and damage sometimes involve lawsuits and expensive court procedure. The court may be asked to establish whether the shipper, the transportation company, or the receiver is responsible for damages. Facts recorded in the inspection certificate issued by the federal-state inspector are accepted as prima-facie evidence in all federal and in most state courts.

Therefore, it is obvious that the benefits of official inspection service are largely those of protection against unjust claims for losses and the satisfaction of insurance that the quality and grade of the product are as agreed on between buyer and seller.

MARKETING

The potato is sufficiently nonperishable that it can be marketed in the raw state every month of the year. The commercial industry in the southern states and in California is based largely on the fact that the crop can be harvested and shipped to market at times when the crop in the northern surplus-producing states is not available. The relatively high prices and the demand for freshly harvested potatoes is usually sufficient to compensate the southern grower for his lower yield and the cost of long-distance shipment. The marketing season begins first in southern Florida, southern Texas, and southern California. Because of its geography and diversity of seasonal climate, California markets potatoes every month of the year, except possibly February and March. The flow of potatoes to market occurs progressively northward from the Gulf states through the so-called intermediate states of North and South Carolina, Kansas, Virginia, and New Jersey to the heavy-producing states of the north. Whenever seasonal weather for planting and harvesting is abnormal, the overlapping of peak harvest results in undesirable competition in the large city markets. Because storage facilities are generally available in the north, the marketing season is much more flexible in the north than in other regions.

Marketing Agencies

Long-distance shipping facilities, regional competition, and consumer demand for well-graded and packaged potatoes have now combined to make the need for special marketing agencies more acute. Small producers can retail directly to local stores, to truckers who come to the farm, at roadside stands, and from house to house. A few large growers supply chain and independent grocers in the smaller cities and villages, others truck to public markets. The principal marketing agencies for commercial growers are farmers' co-operatives, country shippers, and chain store buyers.

Much of the Pennsylvania crop is marketed through the Pennsylvania Potato Growers Association, which operates through local farmers' co-operatives and sells in 50-, 60-, and 15-pound paper sacks under a Keystone brand. The methods and advantages of this system have been discussed in detail by Whitacre (1939); the success of it is contingent on a large and steady volume of uniformly graded potatoes sold on orders assembled and delivered by a central marketing agency.

An increasingly large part of the total crop is marketed by large food chain store companies who buy from wholesale buyers and in turn pack and sell under their own brands.

Advertising Agencies

In states such as Idaho and Maine where a large volume of uniformly graded and packed potatoes is available over a period of several months, producers and marketing organizations find it advantageous to employ an advertising agency. The expense in such case may be borne by a tax levy imposed by state law on each bag processed for market. The benefit is derived largely from advertising the brand in city newspapers, trade papers, and store placards.

Market News Service

An unbiased, cheap, reliable service to keep producers, handlers, and buyers of potatoes informed of supply, price, and demand situations is valuable. Such information is available daily in what is now well known as the Federal-State market news service. The service is free to growers, shippers, and other handlers on application to the headquarters offices of the state departments of agriculture co-operating with the United States Department of Agriculture. Special reports on potatoes alone are issued in the form of mimeographed sheets during the heaviest part of the marketing season. They include information on weather conditions at shipping points, daily carlot shipments from important states during the previous week, market conditions and prices quoted and paid growers at shipping points, carlot arrivals at city terminals from states of origin, and a comparison of the number of carlots marketed to date with the number at the corresponding date of the previous year. All this should guide the producer and the handler in determining the best time to move the crop.

Gross Margins and Price Spreads

It would be difficult to record information on the cost of marketing potatoes. Actual cost figures vary with the completeness of marketing services included. The grower's marketing cost is low because he usually leaves most of the functions of marketing to someone else. The difference between farm price and retail store price is often as much as 100 per cent, depending somewhat on the amount of markup taken by the retailer. The grower-retail price spread on potatoes is usually but not always less than that on fresh vegetables because of greater waste and shrinkage of the latter. The gross margin or price spread between grower receipts and country shippers quotation can be calculated daily from the market news service report. It often varies from 20 to 40 cents the bushel and is more constant than the price of potatoes because shipper's costs are more nearly fixed. The shipper's gross margin must include such items as rental or depreciation on buildings and office space, labor, cost of communication, bags, graders and other processing equipment, insurance, travel, business risks and profit.

Federal Crop Control and Subsidy

To ensure an ample food supply during war years, to stabilize production, and to remove some of the risk carried annually by growers, the federal government in collaboration with the several states instituted a program designed to control the production of potatoes and to subsidize returns to growers. The program was mainly of three phases: (1) acreage control by acreage goals or allotments, (2) price support or guaranteed minimum prices to the grower, and (3) marketing agreements by which the grower contracts with the government to sell only potatoes from his allotted acreage and of a certain grade. Under this program, growers have been encouraged to maintain production, even though in some years at government and therefore at the taxpayers' expense crop surpluses were purchased and later diverted to industrial uses, to feed for livestock, or destroyed. Much of the time, minimum price support to growers has been by law at approximately 90 per cent of the parity index. Parity is a price level supposedly based on the relation of the average cost of things bought by the potato farmer to the price of things he sells. The long-time effect of a price-support program on the potato industry will depend somewhat on the per centage of parity at which potato farm prices are supported.

Market Distribution and Shipping Practices

On a national basis, the potato crop is distributed largely according to the season of production and harvest. Strowbridge (1939) has shown how the forty-eight states fall into four groups according to season of marketing. Thus, there are eleven early potato states, seven intermediate, eighteen surplus late, and twelve other late potato states. States bordering the Atlantic Ocean from North Carolina to Florida, the Gulf states, Tennessee, Arkansas, and Oklahoma comprise the eleven early-crop states. Between the early-

Fig. 125. Loading a refrigerator car with Netted Gem potatoes at Aberdeen, Idaho.

and the late-crop states are Kansas, Missouri, Kentucky, Virginia, Maryland, Delaware, and New Jersey, the seven intermediate crop states. Maine, Idaho, California, New York, North Dakota, Minnesota, Michigan, Wisconsin, Colorado, and Pennsylvania are the principal surplus late potato states. Although New York and California are listed as late-crop states, Long Island and central California produce large quantities of intermediate-crop potatoes and southern California contributes to the early crop.

Potatoes go to market in railroad cars, by motor truck, and by boat. More than ever before, the surplus crop in states closest to large cities is marketed by motor truck. Extent of surplus production is no longer well indicated by total number of carlots of potatoes shipped annually. According to Park (1946), California shipped nearly 30,000 cars of early potatoes in 1944, most of them during the period of April to August inclusive. The early potato shipping states, in order of volume shipped by the more important ones, are California, Florida, New Jersey, Virginia, North Carolina, Louisiana, Colorado, Texas, Alabama, Idaho, Washington, and Oregon.

The methods of precooling, refrigerating, and loading of cars vary according to maturity and condition of the crop, season of shipment, and distance to be shipped. These factors and the diseases involved in spoilage in marketing are discussed and illustrated by Park. Bruising, skinning, and scalding of early, immature tubers predisposes them to later infection and rot by the brown-rot disease. A carload of potatoes is usually a load of 600 bushels or 360 one-hundred-pound burlap bags. Loss of weight in transit of early potatoes shipped from far western and southern states to eastern cities during the summer, and after washing and packing in 100-pound cotton or burlap bags, averages about 1.3 per cent.

There are two common methods of loading 100-pound bags into cars, the pyramid and the aisle method. The aisle system provides for extra air circulation but permits only 300 instead of 360 bags per car. The aisle load consists of three sacks set upright on each side of a center aisle, with horizontal loading three sacks deep on top. In pyramid loading, five sacks are set upright crosswise of the car, three flatwise on top, two flatwise above, to tie in the three, and finally three flatwise in a top layer. This arrangement is commonly referred to as the 5-3-2-3 pyramid load, and, if properly spaced to allow good air circulation, it is probably most satisfactory.

Market Preferences

The quality, variety, and grade of potatoes preferred in various markets naturally varies with price differentials, the income level of the buying public, and the types and qualities of potatoes available. Very often market preference is colored by what the buyer is accustomed to. There is some evidence that people buy more of the better grades and the more expensive varieties when their buying power is high than when it is low. New crop potatoes have a new flavor and a higher sugar content which makes them popular after the old crop is in short supply.

The Russet Burbank or Netted Gem as grown in Idaho is famous throughout the country as a fancy baking potato and sells at a premium price over other varieties because of its high starch content and superior grade and pack. Mimms and Woodbury (1939) reported that during the years 1921 to 1937 on the Chicago market, Idaho Russets sold at a premium ranging from 15 cents to $1.23 per hundredweight over Wisconsin round whites. For the years 1929 to 1937 inclusive, however, the Idaho potato sold at a premium over the Colorado Red McClure only about half the time. Maine-grown Green Mountains are popular in Boston and New York, and Long Island Green Mountains are well known in New York and Philadelphia.

Fig. 126. Carload of 15-pound sacks of Maine potatoes on arrival at the Cleveland terminal market.

Reputation of a variety in a given market is based more on eye appeal, grade, and style of pack than on specific varietal characters. Pullen (1947) studied the relation of grade to price of muck- and upland-grown potatoes in the Buffalo and Rochester markets. He found that the muck-grown crop often met a higher grade standard and sold at a premium of 1 to 8 cents the bushel over upland-grown potatoes. Furthermore, the newer varieties, Katahdin, Chippewa, and Sebago, brought from 3 to 7 cents the bushel more than the older varieties which have less eye appeal.

Wholesale and chain store buyers usually prefer to buy in 100-pound bags while the 15-pound, branded paper sack is the most popular consumer package.

Buying Habits and Per-Capita Consumption

The development of the cash-and-carry or chain store system of merchandising food has brought changes in consumer buying habits. It has resulted in increased packing and selling in consumer packages for the convenience of the retail buyer. It has probably raised the standard of market quality, but selling potatoes in closed packages does not allow shoppers to examine the product. Rasmussen and Childress (1948) reported that 30 to 35 per cent of total sales in upstate New York cities were sold in 10- and 15-pound packages, while in New York City, in 1948, only 14 per cent of the retail operators handled potatoes this way. A similar study by Lee (1948) in Philadelphia showed that about 60 per cent were sold in bulk, nearly 40 per cent being packed in 15-, 10-, 5-, and 50-pound consumer packages. The consumer package offers the advantage of an attractive brand, cleanliness, and a minimum of waste for the retailer. Many retail buyers still prefer the bulk style, however, because it enables them to exercise more choice. In New York city, over nine-tenths of the tonnage sold in consumer packages is handled by food chain stores. Lack of suitable storage is the principal reason why so few people buy in larger, more economical quantities.

Neither the consuming public nor those who handle potatoes know very much about differences in culinary quality among even standard varieties. Eye appeal is more influential than inherent differences in quality in determining choice by buyers. A consumer preference study by Bakken (1934) in the Chicago, Milwaukee, and Madison city markets revealed that 50 to 70 per cent of all retail buyers personally inspected the potatoes before buying. This habit should at least be conducive to the marketing of only the better grades.

During the past 40 years, the per-capita consumption of potatoes in the United States has been decreasing. It is far below that of most of the other important producing countries of the world. Rural people eat more potatoes than do urban. People on farms where the crop is grown eat more potatoes than do people on farms where potatoes are not grown. Since the potato is a food staple, retail price affects consumption very little unless prices are extremely high. Average annual per-capita consumption apparently declined about 35 per cent during the 38-year period 1909–1946, as reported in *The Potato World* (February, 1947) and shown in table 55.

TABLE 55. PER-CAPITA ANNUAL CONSUMPTION OF POTATOES IN THE UNITED STATES.

Year	Pounds	Year	Pounds	Year	Pounds	Year	Pounds
1909	195	1919	153	1929	155	1939	121
1910	197	1920	146	1930	136	1940	130
1911	158	1921	154	1931	140	1941	128
1912	181	1922	154	1932	140	1942	125
1913	185	1923	170	1933	137	1943	133
1914	163	1924	158	1934	138	1944	127
1915	182	1925	153	1935	144	1945	126
1916	142	1926	130	1936	132	1946	126
1917	154	1927	142	1937	126		
1918	173	1928	155	1938	132		

There is no apparent relation between the general price level and potato consumption. The most obvious explanation for the falling off in consumption is the increased amount of fresh vegetables of many kinds and of meat and poultry products eaten during the 38-year period.

Foreign Trade

Potatoes are a relatively bulky, perishable commodity. As a raw product they are not well adapted to long-distance shipment by boat. Furthermore, the United States should be able to consume most of its own production. Our foreign trade in potatoes has been mainly with Canada and is relatively small. According to the United States tariff commission (1946), during the 5-year period 1940–1944, our net exports over imports averaged annually about 360,000 bushels, as shown in table 56.

Imports from Canada vary from a half-million bushels to 5 million bushels, depending largely on the demand for certified seed. The import duty varies from year to year. In 1939, it was, for all potatoes, 60 cents the hundredweight from December 1 to March 1, and thereafter 37.5 cents to November 1. The reduced rate

TABLE 56. UNITED STATES EXPORTS AND IMPORTS OF POTATOES,
1940–1944.

Year	Total Exports	Total Imports	Net Exports over Imports
	(Thousands of Bushels)	(Thousands of Bushels)	(Thousands of Bushels)
1940	2,593	1,324	1,269
1941	2,656	934	1,722
1942	1,764	784	980
1943	2,364	1,128	1,236
1944	1,979	5,388	−3,409
Average	2,271	1,912	360

applies to 1 million bushels of imports except that in years when the United States crop is less than 350 million bushels the quota is increased by the amount of the deficiency.

REFERENCES

Bakken, Henry H. The market for mid-western potatoes. Univ. of Wis. Circ. 272, 1934.

Barger, W. R., G. B. Ramsey, R. L. Perry, and John H. MacGillivray. Handling and shipping tests with new potatoes from Kern County, California. Calif. Agr. Exp. Sta. Bul. 664, 1942.

Hotchkiss, Alida S. Consumer buying of potatoes and store offerings. Cornell Univ. Agr. Exp. Sta. Bul. 764, 1941.

Lee, Wayne A. The quality of potatoes in retail stores. Philadelphia, January 21–February 27, 1948. Pa. State College Jour., Ser. No. 1449, 1948.

Mimms, O. L., and George W. Woodbury. Markets and market preferences for Idaho potatoes. Idaho Agr. Exp. Sta. Bul. 231, 1939.

Poole, Wiley D., and Harold T. Barr. Precooling and drying of washed Irish potatoes. La. Agr. Exp. Sta. Bul. 332, 1941.

Pullen, W. E. Muckland and upland potatoes; grade quality and wholesale price at Buffalo and Rochester. Cornell Univ. Agr. Exp. Sta. Bul. 837, 1947.

Ramsey, G. B., J. M. Lutz, H. O. Werner, and A. D. Edgar. Experiments on shipping washed early potatoes. Neb. Agr. Exp. Sta. Bul. 364, 1944.

Rasmussen, Marius P., and Russell L. Childress. Grade qualities of potatoes in retail stores, New York City, 1948. Cornell Univ., Dept. Agr. Econ. A.E. 675, 1948.

Rinear, E. H. Consumer preferences for potatoes. N.H. Agr. Exp. Sta. Circ. 37, 1931.

Rose, D. H. Handling and shipping early potatoes. U.S. Dept. Agr. Circ. 744, 1946.

Spangler, Raymond L. Standardization and inspection of fresh fruits and vegetables. U.S. Dept. Agr. Misc. Publ. 604, 1946.

Strowbridge, J. W. Origin and distribution of the commercial potato crop. U.S. Dept. Agr. Tech. Bul. 7, rev. 1939.

U.S. Dept. Agr. United States Standards for Potatoes. Service and Regulatory Announcements No. 151, rev. 1942.

U.S. Tariff Commission. Potatoes. War changes in industry series. Report No. 16, 1946.

Vincent, C. L., and H. L. Garver. Potato washing investigations. Wash. Agr. Exp. Sta. Bul. 332, 1936.

Whitacre, W. R. Methods and costs of marketing potatoes in Pennsylvania. Pa. Agr. Exp. Sta. Bul. 372, 1939.

Wood, Marion A. Potatoes in institution food service. Cornell Univ. Agr. Exp. Sta. Bul. 798, 1943.

CHAPTER 15

Quality and Utilization

THE TERM QUALITY as applied to potatoes is commonly used so broadly as to be more or less meaningless. Nevertheless, quality in whatever sense the term is used is of real significance because potatoes are grown and merchandised as a food crop.

Definition

Quality can be defined as a combinaton of factors which relate to the external and internal characters of the tuber. It is good or bad, high or low, depending on the preference of the individual who evaluates it. Quality in potatoes should be considered in three aspects: (1) market quality, (2) culinary or cooking quality, and (3) food quality, that is, for nutritive or health values.

Physical Characters Denoting Quality

In choosing a variety to grow for market and in buying potatoes to eat, one should be familiar with whatever characters represent marketability and texture and color of the cooked product. Too often, quality is judged mainly as a matter of eye appeal and freedom from external defects alone. Quality should also be evaluated on the basis of the use to be made of the product or the method of cooking it. Cleanness, brightness, uniformity of size and shape, regularity of tuber shape, few and shallow eyes, whiteness and smoothness of skin, and whiteness, uniformity, and soundness of flesh are characters which are desirable and indicative of good quality to most people.

Authorities are not entirely agreed as to which of the external characters are most useful in judging internal quality. Deep eyes, irregular shape, and surface defects are all undesirable from the standpoint of waste in preparation, but they do not necessarily indicate poor culinary quality or low food value. Since both starch content and protein content of the tuber increase as it matures, a mature potato should be more mealy than an immature one. Potatoes naturally of netted or flaky skin will show that character as more highly developed when they are mature than when immature. Whiteness and uniformity of flesh indicate that the tuber will cook uniformly and be mealy. When the inner and outer medulla and the cortex are clearly differentiated in a transection of the raw tuber, or when the pith tissue is dark or watery, it is likely that the tuber will slough and will not cook uniformly.

Market Quality

Market quality may be defined as that combination of factors which influences consumer preference or salability in market potatoes. Used in this sense, it includes external or morphological characters only. Most potatoes are not branded by variety name, and neither the retailer nor the consumer knows what variety is being merchandised in most cases. On the contrary a considerable proportion of potatoes sold are labeled as to grade. Grade designation if correctly indicated on the package should be a fair measure of market quality. Unfortunately a large proportion of packaged potatoes labeled No. 1 grade are misbranded. A sampling of potatoes bought by 3125 consumers in Cleveland stores and by 1680 consumers in Rochester, New York, stores during the fall and winter seasons of 1936, 1937, and 1938 was reported by Hotchkiss (1941). A careful grade determination of these samples made by the Department of Vegetable Crops at Cornell showed that an average of only 17 per cent of the total volume bought in Cleveland and 22 per cent of that bought in Rochester were of No. 1 grade.

Similar studies of market quality were made in Philadelphia by Lee (1948) and in New York City by Rasmussen and Childress (1948). In the Philadelphia study, 657 chain and independent stores, or about 13 per cent of the total retail stores, were sampled. The 1242 samples examined by official inspectors for damage and serious damage averaged 14.5 per cent, the average quality being only 1 per cent higher in the chain than in the independent stores and slightly higher in the high than in the low income areas. Over 75 per cent of these samples exceeded the maximum tolerance of 6 per cent damage and were therefore below No. 1 grade. Nearly 60 per cent of these disqualifying defects were old cuts and bruises.

For all retail stores, 52.3 per cent of the samples were marked No. 1 grade, but 74.7 per cent of them were below that grade. In this study, there appeared to be no relation between quality sold and price, although there was an inverse relation between quantity sold and price. Apparently consumers were not offered much choice of quality, or else the profit incentive to pack the better grades was too small. In the New York City survey reported by Rasmussen and Childress (1948), 873 retail stores were sampled for grade defects. Here the average percentage of damaged tubers was 9.2 per cent, or 3.2 per cent more than allowed in No. 1 grade, with cuts and bruises being the principal defects. About 30 per cent were branded as to grade, and almost two-thirds of these failed to meet the requirements for No. 1 grade.

In these and most other studies of market quality, price differentials for various grades average too little to offer a clear-cut inducement for better grading. Percentage defects and size differences seem to affect retail price less than cleanness and brightness.

It has not been possible to show any marked relationship between grade defects and preparation waste. Wood (1943) studied the buying habits and methods of handling of potatoes by 126 institutions in Rochester, New York, New York City, and Cleveland. The majority of these institutions purchased on the basis of No. 1 grade. Her figures on preparation waste for 194 samples show an average of 27 per cent, with practically no difference between samples carrying less than 5-per-cent damage and those showing 25-per-cent or more. Removal of actual damage involved a loss averaging 13 per cent, the remaining 14-per-cent loss being due to removal of the remaining peeling. The percentage of preparation waste in hand peeling was as great as, or greater than, that in machine peeling. Because of the high percentage of waste in peeling, it is not surprising that there appears to be very little correlation between grade or percentage grade defects and preparation waste. It is deplorable, however, that, in peeling potatoes, that portion of the tuber which contains the greatest concentration of protein, carbohydrates, minerals, and vitamins is necessarily lost. This is an argument for cooking potatoes before paring them.

Tuber size is apparently of less importance than defects and appearance. During the fall and winter season of 1938–1939, several hundred housewives in Cleveland, Ohio, and Rochester, New York, were asked about their criticism of the size factor in potatoes bought at retail the week previous to the interview. Over 85 per cent were satisfied. Those who were not satisfied stated a dislike of potatoes more than 3 and less than 2 inches in diameter. A careful size analysis of 417 samples representing these same potatoes showed that over 80 per cent by weight were within the size range 2 to 3 inches in diameter. Only 1.8 per cent were below 1⅞ inch and between 9 and 13 per cent were 3 inches or more in diameter. Therefore, most retail store potatoes met the size requirements of No. 1 grade. Many consumers expressed a preference for a wide range in tuber size so that large tubers could be selected for baking and smaller sizes for other purposes.

Culinary Quality

Color, flavor, and texture of cooked potatoes are characters which appeal to the palate as well as to the eye. A combination of these factors make cooking quality good or bad depending on personal preference. Most people seem to prefer whiteness in cooked potatoes, although yellow-fleshed varieties are widely used in European countries.

Probably the basic reason why the potato is so universally popular as a staple food is its neutral flavor. Whenever its flavor takes on a distinctive character, it is almost certain to displease somebody.

Texture of the cooked product is indicated in terms of mealiness or sogginess; mealiness is usually associated with high starch or high dry-matter content. Probably the most complete review of literature on the subject is that of Sweetman (1936) in which she cites 210 published articles and concludes that "published reports of research of factors affecting the cooking quality of potatoes contain many conflicting statements." The reasons for such conflict are: (1) many environmental factors affect quality, (2) the measurements of quality are subjective, chemical, and mechanical, and (3) there is often much variation between tubers grown and stored under identical conditions.

Specific gravity is one of the best measures of starch and dry matter in potato tubers. Prince et al. (1940) showed that starch content can be predetermined within 1 or 2 per cent by specific gravity. In testing potatoes grown in several soil types in New Hampshire, they found that increasing the phosphorous content of the fertilizer increased the specific gravity. Smith and Nash (1940) got a lower specific gravity when the application of 5-10-5 fertilizer exceeded 1500 pounds to the acre. Supplementing a 1000-pound application of 5-10-5 fertilizer with the nitrogen equivalent of 12 tons of stable manure also decreased the specific gravity and the mealiness below that resulting from smaller applications. Soil reaction also may affect mealiness. A soil of low pH value usually results in less mealiness than one less acid. This may be the indirect effect of more soluble intercellular material which holds the tissue together when it is cooked.

The inherent starch content and mealiness of different varieties has been discussed in Chapter 8. The mechanics of mealiness is not well established. Formerly, it was thought that high starch content was associated with mealiness, because it caused a rupture of cell walls when the starch granules expanded on cooking. More recently the theory of cell rupture has been discarded in favor of the theory that mealiness is associated with the ease of cell separation depending on the solubility of the pectins or protopectins of the middle lamella between the cells. A reliable qualitative test for pectin should help to determine the validity of the theory of cell separation. Potassium pectate is relatively soluble, but calcium pectate is not. Theoretically, a high-lime soil or one of high pH should produce a soggy potato, and one of high potash content should give a mealy potato. Nevertheless, in practice, large applications of potash in the fertilizer tend to lower the starch content of the tubers. This discrepancy has been explained by Personius and Sharp (1939), who showed that the application of heat of cooking, especially in a very acid solution, not only favors hydrolysis but also softens the pectic material between the cells and lessens the adhesion of the cells.

For predetermining the specific gravity of potato tubers, a convenient method is to float them in salt brine of various known concentrations. The more readily a tuber sinks in such solutions, the higher its specific gravity and the mealier it is. A tuber having a specific gravity less than 1.060 is likely to be soggy when cooked; one having a specific gravity of 1.100 or higher should be very mealy. The amount of table salt per gallon of water corresponding to various specific gravities at which each tuber will barely float is indicated in table 57.

TABLE 57. SALT BRINE SOLUTIONS FOR MEASURING SPECIFIC GRAVITY.

Specific Gravity	Table Salt per Gallon of Water		Mealiness of Cooked Potatoes
	Grams	Ounces	
1.050	282	9.94	Soggy
1.060	340	11.96	Soggy
1.070	397	13.99	Fairly mealy
1.080	455	16.01	Fairly mealy
1.090	512	18.04	Mealy
1.100	524	18.44	Very mealy

A common criticism of boiled potatoes is their tendency to darken soon after removal from the cooking water. This fact early led to the assumption that the tendency to blacken was due either to oxidation of some component of the tuber or to activation of some enzyme as a result of oxidation. Smith (1937) reported that potatoes grown at a soil reaction of pH 7.92 are usually more attractive in color than those grown at a lower pH. Contrary to the conclusions of several other workers, he found no evidence that blackening is due to a deficiency of potash in the soil.

Smith and Nash (1938) grew Rural type potatoes in greenhouse sand cultures with nutrient cultures, each minus one of the minor elements, copper, manganese, boron, iron, and magnesium. There appeared to be no effect on color, form, or texture of the cooked tubers from a deficiency of these elements. Poorest flavor resulted where no iron, boron, or copper was added to the culture solution. In a later field experiment these workers tested the effect of adding boron at the rate of 20 pounds of borax to the acre. Here it was found that the addition of boron to the soil caused the tubers to slough much less and to have a much better flavor than those grown without the addition of boron.

The cause of darkening of cooked potatoes has for a long time been controversial and still is. Nutting and Pfund (1942) worked with a lot of potatoes very susceptible to blackening and, after cooking and cooling them in inert or oxygen-free air, decided that darkening is essentially an oxidation process. However, they concluded that it could not be the formation of the pigment melanin as the result of activation of the enzyme tyrosinase because the heat

of cooking would destroy this enzyme. Such a conclusion may not
be justified, because the necessary enzyme reaction may occur before rather than after cooking. These workers demonstrated also
that darkening could be largely avoided by acidifying the cooking
water with such weak acids as citric acid and vinegar. However, they
found that by acidifying the water to a pH value of 4.1 or less to
prevent darkening, a thick, tough layer of tissue was formed on the
outside of the tubers. In cooking potatoes that have a marked
tendency to blacken, this tough outer layer may be preferable to
the discoloration.

Fig. *127*. Blackening of boiled potatoes. *Left:* from plants grown in normal
light. *Right:* from shaded plants. (After L. B. Nash, Cornell University.)

In a series of experiments conducted in 1940 by Smith *et al.*
(1942), 232 samples of potatoes grown in six different regions of
New York were examined for discoloration after boiling. These
authors found that little or no blackening occurred in samples
which matured under mean temperatures of 70° F. or higher, and
that samples which matured under mean temperatures of 60° F.
or lower usually blackened. They were able to prevent practically
all blackening of susceptible tubers by exposing them to temperatures of 100° F. for 3 or 4 days. Also there was a high correlation
between hydrogen ion concentration of tuber tissue and the degree
of blackening, the relationship being negative. In tubers or in
varieties that tend to darken after cooking, the stem end has a lower

acidity and tends to darken more than the apical end. These workers therefore concluded that blackening can be reduced by storage at high temperatures and by boiling in certain acidified solutions.

Tottingham *et al.* (1947), pioneer workers on the problem of blackening, after 9 years of study that included research on various soil types, fertilizer treatments, climatic conditions, strains, and varieties, decided that no single factor is uniformly responsible, and that variety more than any other factor governs the tendency to darken. They cite Triumph, Chippewa, and Sebago as varieties which rarely blacken and Rurals and Cobblers as especially susceptible. This differs from the conclusions of Smith *et al.* (1942) who believe that early planting or any other means of ensuring early maturity under relatively high temperatures, including the selection of early varieties, is the best means of control.

Graying is another form of darkening which may occur in potatoes dehydrated for preservation and long-distance shipment as in the war years. Smith and Kelly (1944) devised a method of prevention by preheating at 165° to 212° F. for a few minutes prior to peeling, and later blanching the prepared pieces for 5 minutes at 212° F. in a solution acidified to pH 4.0 with ortho-phosphoric acid.

Nutritive Values

The health values of the potato are measured in terms of calories, heat units or fuel energy per pound consumed, and by its content of minerals and vitamins. As stated in a previous chapter, potatoes are a good source of phosphorus, potassium, and iron. They rate high as a cheap source of carbohydrate or energy food, because of their high starch content and their high per-capita consumption. In caloric value, they provide 385 calories per pound of raw product. This is equivalent to 85 calories per 100 grams. Potatoes as such are essentially not fattening except as they are eaten with generous amounts of butter and gravy. Unlike meats and many other foods which increase the acidity of body fluids, they have a potential reserve alkalinity of about 9 cc. of alkali per 100 grams.

As a source of vitamins, the potato is a good source of B (thiamine) and of C (ascorbic acid), a poor source of A and B_2 (riboflavin), and has no D. One hundred grams of raw potato contain 8 to 60 I. U. of vitamin B_1, 0.012 mg. of B_2, and 3.1 to 33 mgs. of C. Numerous factors influence the actual content of minerals and vitamins, some of which will be discussed here.

Potatoes furnish bulk to the diet, a factor said to be necessary to good health through regulation of the digestive tract. Potato starch is more digestible than that of most other common food sources. One medium-sized tuber furnishes enough bases to neutralize the acids of two average slices of roast beef. Substitution of rice for potatoes would not accomplish this function as rice produces an acidifying effect.

Methods of preparation and of cooking may greatly affect food values and loss of constituents. A common practice is to peel old potatoes and to soak them in water for rather long periods. This may result in less darkening of the flesh, but it is certain to result in some loss of valuable minerals and vitamins. Baking and steaming at rather high temperatures are methods of cooking most conservative of food values. Boiling after peeling, especially if the peeled tubers are soaked long in cold water, is most wasteful of nutrients. Both protein and iron are lost by soaking in water and by boiling in the peeled form.

According to Stiebeling (1932) potatoes contain from 0.0008 to 0.0016 per cent of iron and rank with green beans, cabbage, and green lettuce as a good source. Pfund and Nutting (1942) studied the effect of method of cooking on loss of iron, using potatoes of the Rural type. On the average, the loss of iron as a result of cooking, ranged from 0.01 to 0.03 mg. per 100 gms. Steaming resulted in less loss than boiling, unpeeled tubers lost less iron than those peeled, and salting the cooking water seemed to have no effect on the loss.

Sloughing of the outer layer when peeled potatoes are boiled is a common source of loss of food value; it is often the subject of criticism by the housewife. It is probably but not necessarily true that high-starch varieties slough worse than low-starch ones. A tuber in which the cortical layer is distinctly whiter than the medullary areas is almost certain to slough, unless it is cooked without peeling, because the outer layer will break down before the inner portion is done. To minimize sloughing, care should be taken to boil the water more slowly, or the potatoes should be cooked in their jackets. Acidifying the water should also help to prevent sloughing of peeled potatoes by toughening the outer tissue.

A large proportion of the people living in the north temperate zone of America and Europe depend on the potato as their chief source of energy food and of minerals and vitamins. This is particularly true of farmers and people of relatively low income, because of their particularly high consumption of potatoes. The approximate amount of energy, protein, calcium, iron, and certain vitamins available in an average serving of potatoes was reported by Esselen *et al.* (1942) and is shown in table 58.

TABLE 58. NUTRIENTS SUPPLIED BY ONE AVERAGE SERVING OF POTATOES (5¼ OUNCES OR 150 GRAMS).

Nutrient	Daily Requirement (for an Active 155-lb. Man)	Amount in One Serving	Per Cent of Daily Requirement in One Serving
Energy	3000 calories	127.5 calories	4.2
Protein	70 grams	3.0 grams	4.3
Calcium	0.8 gram	0.019 gram	2.4
Iron	12.0 mgs.	1.65 mgs.	13.7
Vitamin B$_1$	1.8 mgs.	0.195 mg.	10.8
Vitamin B$_2$	2.7 mgs.	0.090 mg.	3.3
Vitamin C	75.0 mgs.	10.00 mgs.	13.3

Potatoes are an excellent source of vitamin C, but research workers have found this vitamin to be quite unstable. Therefore the actual content of vitamin C at any given time for any variety or lot of tubers depends largely on when the determination is made and the previous conditions of handling. Recent and extensive work on this subject has been done by Kelly and Somers (1948) at the U.S. Plant, Soil, and Nutrition Laboratory at Ithaca, N.Y. They found that the ascorbic acid content of the tubers increases slowly and as much as 50 per cent during their period of development. However, it decreases rapidly after the tuber matures, in fact about 50 per cent during the first 2 months of storage and as much as 70 per cent for the first 6 months of storage. These results represent the average for six varieties and five storage temperatures. These workers also found a marked effect of both storage temperature and of variety on vitamin-C content of tubers. High storage temperature favors its retention, there being a higher content at 50° F. after 4 months' storage than at 40° F. after 2 months. The Katahdin and Warba varieties rated high, Green Mountain intermediate, and

Chippewa low in ascorbic acid. Sometimes early varieties have been analyzed and rated low not because of their inherent quality but because they matured early and had subsequently lost a part of the vitamin.

The work of Kelly and Somers largely substantiates that of May-field *et al.* (1937) and of Esselen *et al.* (1942). The latter found that all methods of cooking caused some destruction of ascorbic acid, the loss varying from 31 to 80 per cent, depending on the method of cooking. Boiling the tubers in salted water rather than in plain water resulted in about 4 per cent less loss.

UTILIZATION

The principal use of potatoes in the United States always has been as human food. As such, potatoes lead all other fresh vegetables in terms of land area used, volume produced, and total farm value. City market vegetable surveys in the large eastern cities indicate that potatoes comprise about one-third of the total tonnage of fresh vegetables handled during August and nearly one-half in December, when there are fewer other vegetables to compete. The consumption of raw potatoes for human food is, however, much higher in north European countries, and usage for industrial purposes and for livestock feed is greater there than in this country.

According to Treadway (1948), of a normal United States crop of 375 million bushels, 81 per cent is used for food, 5 per cent for seed, and 14 per cent for nonfood purposes. Each year the United States Department of Agriculture publishes figures on the farm disposition of the crop produced in the thirty-seven late and intermediate states. For the crop of 1946 these figures showed that 79.6 per cent was sold or for sale, 9.5 per cent was used and saved for food in the farm household, 6.7 per cent was fed to livestock or lost by shrinkage after harvest, and 4.1 per cent was saved for seed on the farms where grown. As the per-capita consumption for food in the raw state has declined and production has become more centralized and specialized, the trend has been toward processing a larger percentage of the crop for food and industrial uses.

Processed Food

Potatoes are now processed for food in the form of chips, flour or meal, and starch, and as dehydrated, canned, and frozen. Treadway states that the manufacture of potato chips is increasing, about

20 million bushels or 4 per cent of the crop being processed in this form. Potato flour and meal are used in bread, soups, gravies, and as a breading agent. The difference between flour and meal is that the former is somewhat more refined. Dehydrated potatoes are used for mashed potatoes and in meat and vegetable stews. Potatoes are canned as salad, whole small boiled, diced, Julienne strips, and soup. They are frozen as French fried, raw slices, and mashed. About 7 per cent of the crop is fed to livestock and poultry in the fresh form, as silage, and dehydrated for use in feeds. The principal industrial uses are for starch, alcohol, and glucose. Potato starch is used for sizing textiles and paper and for dextrin and plastics.

Potato Chips

Potatoes, as processed food, are most popular in the form of potato chips. Chip factories are numerous throughout the country and vary greatly in size. The principal problem is so to choose and handle the raw product as to get a bright-colored chip with a minimum of waste. The Russet Rural variety is preferred for this purpose by most chip makers. Denny and Thornton (1940) tested many varieties and found that those with the lowest content of reducing sugar were most satisfactory. Among these were Russet Rural, Chippewa, Carman No. 3, Irish Cobbler, and Katahdin. Second choice included Russet Burbank and Early Ohio, whereas Bliss Triumph and Green Mountain gave a dark-colored product. Various tests have been developed to predetermine the suitability of a variety or sample by measuring its content of reducing sugar. The content of reducing sugar can be controlled or reduced by storage of the raw product at relatively high temperature for a few days prior to processing.

The successive steps in chip manufacture are (1) "curing" the raw tubers at a temperature of 70° F. or above for at least two weeks, (2) sampling or plugging to test for color of the processed chip, (3) peeling with an abrasive mechanical peeler, (4) slicing into thin, uniform slices, (5) washing to remove loose starch, (6) cooking in a shortening of vegetable oil, (7) drying, (8) packaging in waxed paper bags, and (9) packaging in corrugated pasteboard cartons wrapped in pliofilm to protect against the absorption of moisture. Treadway (1947) has provided a fairly complete review of the commercial development of the more important potato by-products to date. He stated that an average of 25.8 pounds of chips are made from each 100 pounds of raw potatoes, and that the per-capita consumption of chips in 1946 was 1.8 pounds.

Potato Starch

The oldest industrial use of potatoes is for starch. About the middle of the nineteenth century there were 150 starch factories in New England, Ohio, Michigan, Wisconsin, and Minnesota. Later, competition with cornstarch reduced the number to only a few in

Fig. 128. Plant at Twin Falls, Idaho, where No. 2 grade potatoes were processed as shreds and packed in 25-pound drums for conversion by U.S. Army into mashed potatoes.

Maine and Minnesota. Today the potato starch industry is increasing as a means of disposal of the surplus crop in the more intensive producing areas. The equipment for and the method of making potato starch have been described in detail by Beresford and Aslett (1945) and by Brautlecht (1940). A fairly large and steady supply of surplus or off-grade potatoes is necessary to the construction and profitable operation of a potato starch factory. For this reason, most of the plants are now located in Maine and Idaho.

Other Products

Most of the potato flour and meal is manufactured in Idaho where sound, clean tubers of the Russet Burbank or Netted Gem variety are available. The methods of manufacture of the two are very similar, the difference being mainly that for meal the skin is used, for flour the tubers are peeled before cooking. About 5 pounds of raw potatoes are required to make 1 pound of flour or meal. This means that 1 pound of meal or flour will reconstitute to 5 pounds of steamed, cooked potatoes. Prices of potato flour can be estimated as from 1.5 to 2.0 times those of potato starch. The percentage composition of potato flour or meal averages as follows: water 6.9 to 15.2, crude protein 5.1 to 6.6, fat 0.1, carbohydrates 72.5 to 81.6, crude fiber 1.3 to 1.9, ash 3.7 to 5.0. In processing, the raw potatoes are thoroughly washed, steam-cooked and roller-dried, the skin being rubbed off in the roller process to retain the full nutritive value of the raw tuber. Grinding and sacking complete the process.

In canning potatoes, only small, whole, sound tubers are used; they are preserved in a weak brine solution. They are first washed, then peeled and steamed. The ratio of raw to processed product is about 3 to 1.

A large volume of potatoes was dehydrated during the war years for foreign shipment. Since then, this method of processing has decreased, and most of the dehydrated product is used in livestock feeds. It has a composition very much like corn, the composition averaging 10 per cent moisture, 74.4 per cent carbohydrates, 9.0 per cent protein, and 0.4 per cent fat. With corn at $2.00 the bushel, potatoes for dehydration would be worth about $8.70 the ton.

The potato has not been able to compete successfully with corn, molasses, and grains as a source of industrial alcohol in this country. Only a very few plants are being operated for this purpose. The process consists of washing the raw tubers, cooking and cooling to the temperature at which malt converts the starch to sugar. The sugars are then fermented to alcohol by yeast, and finally the alcohol is distilled from the mash. One hundred pounds of potatoes will produce about 1 gallon of 190-proof alcohol.

Feed for Livestock

Normally from 5 to 7 per cent of the potato crop is fed to livestock. This has been the convenient and the economical way to dispose of cull and low-grade potatoes which would be a liability on the retail food markets, and which would probably spoil otherwise. Potatoes may be fed raw, cooked, or as ensilage in combination with grass or corn silage. They may be fed to all classes of livestock including poultry and horses, provided they are not fed in excess and are used only as a supplement to other feeds. F. B. Morrison and K. L. Turk at the Cornell University Experiment Station are authority for the following recommendations on feeding potatoes to livestock.

Potatoes are satisfactory for feeding to dairy cows, beef cattle, sheep, swine, and horses, in limited amounts, as a substitute for part of the grain as commonly used. They are fed raw to all classes of livestock except hogs. For hogs, it is both advisable and profitable to cook or steam the potatoes. When cooked, the potatoes should be salted and the water thrown away because it is quite bitter. About 300 pounds of potatoes will supply as much total digestible nutrients as will 100 pounds of alfalfa hay. In other words, potatoes are worth about one-third as much as alfalfa hay. For furnishing digestible nutrients, it takes about 400 to 450 pounds of potatoes to equal 100 pounds of an average grain mixture. Potatoes can be safely fed, in amounts not exceeding 35 pounds per head daily, with good results to milking cows. For horses, potatoes may be used to replace part of the concentrate feed. Small quantities, 3 to 5 pounds daily, seem to have a beneficial effect on the general condition of horses.

A comparison of the digestible nutrients furnished by potatoes and other feeds as given by Morrison and Turk is shown in table 59.

TABLE 59. DIGESTIBLE NUTRIENTS IN POTATOES AND OTHER FEEDS.

Feeds	Dry Matter	Digestible Crude Protein	Total Digestible Nutrients	Nutritive Ratio, 1:
Raw potatoes	21.2	1.1	17.1	14.5
Corn silage, well matured	26.3	1.1	17.7	15.1
Wet brewers' grains	24.1	4.6	16.7	2.6
Wet beet pulp	9.3	0.5	7.4	13.8
Corn, No. 2	85.2	7.1	81.7	10.4

Fed to poultry, cooked potatoes make a valuable addition to the ration for winter layers. Raw potatoes are not satisfactory. A suitable method is to mix enough boiled or steamed potatoes in the laying mash to make a moist, crumbly mixture. Fed in this manner, about 6 to 10 pounds of potatoes to each 100 hens will be required daily.

Solanine Poisoning

Solanine is defined as an amorphous alkaloid having the formula $C_{52} H_{83} NO_{13}$. Old potatoes held in storage and particularly those that have developed a greenish color are commonly thought to have a high solanine content and to be poisonous if eaten in appreciable quantity. It is generally believed that solanine is more prominent in old potatoes and especially in potato sprouts than in new potatoes. The fact that potato tubers are sunburned does not necessarily mean that their content of solanine is high. All members of the plant family Solanaceae contain more or less of this chemical substance.

Mayfield *et al.* (1937) analyzed Netted Gem and Bliss Triumph potatoes stored in cool damp and in warm dry storage from August to May and found that type of storage had no influence on solanine content. However, the solanine content did increase from the immature-plant stage to the late-storage period, and it ranged from 0.008 per cent in August to 0.057 per cent in May.

Hansen (1919) in Germany stated that the alleged solanine poisoning from potatoes is not due to solanine but to some form of bacterial toxin. In the gastrointestinal tract it undergoes hydrolysis with the formation of solanidine which is practically insoluble and therefore cannot be absorbed into the blood stream. Large quantities of decomposed, sprouted, and sunburned potatoes and potato sprouts were fed to dairy cows at both the Idaho and the North Dakota Experiment Stations without any evidence of toxic symptoms. In similar feeding experiments with rats and guinea pigs at the Montana Station where potatoes high in solanine were used, no toxic symptoms resulted. It therefore appears that there is very little danger of solanine poisoning from feeding greened or sprouted potatoes to livestock.

REFERENCES

Beresford, Hobart, and Marvin J. Aslett. Potato starch production in Idaho. Idaho Agr. Exp. Sta. Bul. 259, 1945.

Brautlecht, C. A. Manufacture of white potato starch in the United States. Maine Agr. Exp. Sta. Misc. Paper 562, 1940.

Cobb, J. S. A study of culinary quality in white potatoes. Amer. Potato Jour. 12, No. 12, 1935.

Denny, F. E., and Norwood C. Thornton. Factors for color in the production of potato chips. Contrib. Boyce Thompson Inst. 11, No. 4, 1940.

Esselen, William B., Jr., Mary E. Lyons, and Carl E. Fellers. The composition and nutritive value of potatoes with special emphasis on vitamin C. Mass. Agr. Exp. Sta. Bul. 390, 1942.

Hansen, J. Solanine and its occurrence in potatoes and potato skins with special reference to the poisoning question. Ztschr. Exp. Path. Therap. 20, 385. Abstracted in Chem. Abs. 16, 3143, 1919.

Hotchkiss, Alida S. Consumer buying of potatoes and store offerings. Cornell Univ. Agr. Exp. Sta. Bul. 764, 1941.

Kelly, W. C., and G. F. Somers. Studies on vitamin C (ascorbic acid) in potatoes. Unpublished material, U.S. Plant, Soil, and Nutrition Laboratory, Ithaca, N.Y., 1948.

Lee, Wayne A. The quality of potatoes in retail stores. Philadelphia, January 21–February 27, 1948. Pa. State College Jour., Ser. No. 1449, 1948.

Mayfield, Helen L., Jessie E. Richardson, Ruth J. Davis, and Erlene J. Andes. The effect of winter storage on the palatability and vitamin content of potatoes grown in Montana. Mont. Agr. Exp. Sta. Bul. 346, 1937.

Nutting, Helen West, and Marion Pfund. Nature of darkening of cooked potatoes. Food Research 7, No. 1, 1942.

Personius, Catherine J., and Paul F. Sharp. Adhesion of potato-tissue cells as influenced by pectic solvents and precipitants. Food Research 4, No. 3, 1939.

Pfund, Marion C., and Helen West Nutting. Iron content of potatoes as influenced by cooking method. Food Research 7, No. 3, 1942.

Prince, Ford S., Paul T. Blood, W. H. Coates, and Thomas G. Phillips. Experiments with potatoes. N.H. Agr. Exp. Sta. Bul. 324, 1940

Rasmussen, Marius P, and Russell L. Childress. Grade qualities of potatoes in retail stores, New York City, 1948. Cornell Univ., Dept. Agr. Econ. A.E. 675, 1948.

Smith, Ora. Some factors affecting culinary quality of potatoes. Amer. Potato Jour. 14, No. 7, 1937.

Smith, Ora, and L. B. Nash. Effect of certain minor elements on chemical composition and cooking quality of potato tubers. Amer. Soc. Hort. Sci. Proc., 1938.

Smith, Ora, and L. B. Nash. Potato Quality I. Relation of fertilizers and rotation systems to specific gravity and cooking quality. Amer. Potato Jour. 17, No. 7, 1940.

Smith, Ora, L. B. Nash, and A. L. Dittmann. Potato Quality VI. Relation of temperature and other factors to blackening of boiled potatoes. Amer. Potato Jour. 19, No. 11, 1942.

Smith, Ora, and W. C. Kelly. How to prevent graying of potatoes during dehydration. Food Packer, Sept., 1944.

Stiebeling, Hazel K. The iron content of vegetables and fruits. U.S. Dept. Agr. Circ. 205, 1932.

Sweetman, Marion Deyoe. Factors affecting the cooking qualities of potatoes. Maine Agr. Exp. Sta. Bul. 383, 1936.

Tottingham, W. E., Rudolph Nagy, A. Frank Ross, Jerry W. Marek, and Carl O. Clogett. Blackening indices of potatoes grown under various conditions of field culture. Jour. Agr. Research 74, Nos. 5 and 6, 1947.

Treadway, R. H. Industrial utilization of cull and surplus potatoes. Amer. Potato Jour. 24, No. 11, 1947.

Treadway, R. H. Utilization of white potatoes. Amer. Potato Jour. 25, No. 8, 1948.

Wood, Marion A. Potatoes in institution food service. Cornell Univ. Agr. Exp. Sta. Bul. 798, 1943.

CHAPTER 16

Breeding and Improvement

THE NEED FOR IMPROVEMENT of potatoes is proportionate to the demands of producers and consumers for characters not available in existing varieties. Growers find it increasingly necessary to have higher-yielding varieties to get greater returns for their labor and investment in land and equipment, to satisfy the demand for more intensive food production, and to compete more successfully with other farm enterprises. The standards of quality change continuously as the standard of living of consumers changes and consumers are able to avail themselves of an ever-increasing variety of food products. As new disease and insect pests appear and old ones increase in severity, the need for resistant varieties and varieties adapted to new situations increases. New methods of processing and preserving potatoes and new industrial uses force the need to find varieties appropriately adapted. For these and other reasons the work of the breeder and the seed grower is never done. Several methods of potato improvement are available to meet these objectives. Those most commonly used are breeding or hybridization and clonal selection.

Hybridization

During the past 20 years, most of the improvement in potato varieties has been accomplished by artificial or controlled hybridization. Until then, this method was limited in scope by the lack of viable pollen in desirable parent stocks. Pollen sterility was common to most cultivated varieties except a few which were poor in market quality. Stuart (1921) reported that, between 1903 and 1920, Early Silverskin, Irish Seedling, Keeper, McCormick, and Round Pinkeye were the best pollen parents available, while such good varieties as Burbank, Green Mountain, Rural, Cobbler, Triumph, Early Rose, Early Ohio, and Pearl rarely produced viable pollen. In an experiment with paper mulch in 1928, the present author, using the Rural variety, harvested 112 seed balls. Examination showed that every fruit was parthenocarpic, not a single seed being formed although remnants of ovules were found in a few. The average diameter of the fruits was 1.22 centimeters, the range being 0.8 to 2.2 centimeters.

Inheritance of Male Sterility

In 1910 Salaman reported that male sterility is inherited as a dominant Mendelian character. According to Langley and Clark (1930), wild species usually produce viable pollen whereas cultivated varieties produce viable pollen rarely. This lack of viable pollen is largely responsible for the nonproduction of seed in potatoes, and although the cause of sterility is not known it is associated with irregular chromosome behavior at the time of meiotic segregation. These authors stated that the chromosome number in the genus Solanum is always in multiples of 12. They found the haploid number to be 24 in 37 varieties of *S. tuberosum,* most of the wild species carrying a greater or less number. The number and behavior of chromosomes in our cultivated varieties indicate that they are of mixed ancestry derived from two or more species. Krantz, Becker, and Fineman (1939), in studying the inheritance of pollen sterility, used stainability as a means of differentiating between viable and nonviable pollen. "Observations on 2786 individuals from 101 selfed lines indicated that 47.8 per cent flowered and 60.9 per cent of the flowering individuals set fruit. Failure of the other 39.1 per cent of flowering plants to set fruit may possibly have been due to environmental factors." These authors suggest that there may be sufficient antagonism between fruit production and growth of the vegetative organs so that growth of vegetative organs and selection for high yield of tubers have tended to eliminate the profusely blossoming and highly fruitful types. Selection for high yield has favored retention of genes adversely influencing sexual reproduction.

Becker (1939) reported results of inheritance studies of crosses of *S. demissum* (72 diploid chromosomes) × *S. tuberosum* (48 diploid chromosomes). The F_1 hybrid had 60 chromosomes, but the sterility in the F_1 generation was high, only 3 plants being fertile enough to produce seed. One of these resembled *S. demissum* and was uniform; the other two resembled *S. tuberosum* and were variable in chromosome number. *Solanum demissum* is a small plant, prostrate in growth habit, with small, elongated leaflets; it is late in maturity and produces long stolons and many small tubers. Found only in Mexico, it is in demand for breeding as it carries genes for both frost resistance and resistance to late blight.

Johnstone (1939) recognized the possibility that new gene combinations and forms might be obtained, and pollen fertility and crossability of wild with cultivated species might be increased by treatment with colchicine to induce polyploidy. He was successful in doubling the chromosome numbers in Russet Rural, Golden, three seedlings, and five wild species by treating the seed in 1.0-, 0.5-, and 0.25-per-cent aqueous solutions of colchicine in petri dishes for 72 hours. The treatments produced various effects on the habit of growth of the plants depending on the species involved, but nearly all plants were normal. An effect common to most of the treated plants was enlarged stomates by which it was fairly easy to distinguish the tetraploids from the normal diploids.

Breeding Environment

It is well known that the potato plant blossoms most profusely in the cooler regions of the North. A majority of varieties have been developed in New England, New York, Michigan, and Minnesota by such notables breeders as Goodrich, Burbank, Pringle, Bressee, Carman, Stuart, Clark, Stevenson, Reddick, and Krantz. Cool climate favors the development of flowers and fruit, although it may not be associated with the production of viable pollen. High temperatures seem to favor the premature abscission of flower buds. Werner (1942) of Nebraska has shown that, under greenhouse conditions, the most extensive blossom, fruit, and seed production occurs when a light intensity of about 500 foot-candles at the top of the plants is used for supplemental light during a full 24-hour photoperiod.

Many growers assume that failure of potatoes to blossom under field conditions is an indication that the yield of tubers will be reduced. This is not necessarily so even though conditions unfavorable for blossoming are also unfavorable for tuber development.

Inheritance of Characters

Because of limitations imposed by pollen sterility and lack of desirable parent stocks, the study of Mendelian inheritance of characters has been slow and difficult. Irregularity of chromosome behavior, particularly in interspecies crosses, has complicated the problem and delayed results. However, the mode of inheritance of a few plant characters and of resistance to several diseases and insects is now known.

Hayes and Immer (1942), while citing the importance of self-fertility in clones used for breeding, state that self-fruitfulness in itself leads to a loss in yield of tubers, and that therefore it should be bred out of the ultimate progeny. This seems a doubtful conclusion in that most of our newer varieties are not only high-yielding but also highly fruitful. Examples are Katahdin, Houma, Chippewa, and Sebago.

Inheritance of skin color is of much interest, but its mode of inheritance is complicated, and it is very subject to mutation. Several varieties were originated as mutants by loss of skin color; other varieties, less commonly, by the addition of color. Color of tuber skin is sometimes borne only in the inner periderm, sometimes only in the outer cortex, and sometimes in both. Krantz and Mattson (1936) indicated that, when color is borne in either area alone, its inheritance is governed by three complementary factors differing for each area, and when color is borne in both areas, an independent set of factors is involved. Blue color of periderm and cortex is governed by two factors, each capable of changing red periderm and red cortex to blue.

Blight resistance has been difficult of accomplishment because of the sterility resulting from the necessary interspecific crosses involved. Stevenson *et al.* (1937) say that blight resistance in our cultivated varieties is inherited as a recessive character, controlled probably by multiple genes. Pollen sterility apparently is a dominant character in view of the high percentage of sterile progeny in F_1 hybrids resulting where both male-sterile and male-fertile parent stocks are used.

The small amount of evidence available indicates that qualitative characters of tuber such as starch content, protein, and dry matter

are not inherited in simple Mendelian fashion but are an example
of blended inheritance in which multiple genes are involved.

Disease and Insect Resistance

The development of resistant varieties appears to offer the most
satisfactory means of controlling potato diseases and insects. Pest
control is both expensive and unsatisfactory when it depends solely
on fungicides, insecticides, and sanitary practices. However, breeding for resistance to one pest not only has been difficult to accomplish, but, once attained, the variety or strain may be so lacking in
other desirable characters as to have little commercial value.
Several scab-resistant varieties have low market quality.

The effort to obtain immunity to late blight has been a long
struggle. The first known measure of real success came to Reddick
(1943), who developed a method of breeding subsequent to the
discovery that S. demissum, a wild species found only in Central
Mexico, carried immunity to this disease. As previously stated, S.
demissum has 72 diploid chromosomes, S. tuberosum 48. In cross-
ing these two species, sterility in the F₁ progeny presented a problem.
By using S. demissum as the female parent, Reddick had very little
difficulty in producing fertile crosses. This species sets seed freely,
although its pollen is rarely effective on domestic varieties. Segregation in the F₂ is uncommon in that most of the progeny resemble
S. demissum. To get back the type common to domestic varieties,
Reddick backcrossed the F₁ progeny with pollen of a domestic variety different from the original male parent. As a result of Reddick's
method, he has produced at least twelve varieties highly resistant to
late blight and most of them high yielding. These include Empire,
Placid, Virgil, Chenango, Ashworth, Essex, Snowdrift, and Fillmore.
A similar result has been attained by R. V. Akeley and F. J. Stevenson of the U.S. Department of Agriculture in the creation of
Kennebec, a highly resistant, high-yielding variety developed from
a race of potatoes imported from Germany.

Through a national potato breeding program, promising seedlings developed for disease resistance and improved quality by the
Department and by several state experiment stations have been
tested and several of them named and introduced. Since the introduction of Katahdin in 1934, about forty varieties have been

named for commercial use. These have been listed as to year of introduction by Tolaas (1947).

In breeding for scab resistance, Krantz and Eide (1948) established a method of measuring resistance in terms of scab indices. These indices ranged from (1)—shallow lesions—to (5)—deep pitted lesions—and were typified by (1) Hindenburg, (2) Jubel, Menominee, Ontario, (3) intermediate (no example available), (4) Sebago, (5) Cobbler, Chippewa. Selection of individual plants in seedling families in the scab test plot was relatively ineffective in isolating scab-resistant seedlings. However, by growing four hills of a clone in a heavily infested test plot, a reliable indication of scab resistance was obtained.

The aphid, responsible for transmission of a number of virus diseases under field conditions, is difficult to control. Therefore inherent or natural plant resistance to aphids is highly desirable. Certain varieties are notably resistant, others highly susceptible. Adams (1946) in New Brunswick, Canada, compared many varieties and seedlings in their susceptibility to injury by the aphid *Myzus persicae* Sulzer. Single-stemmed plants were grown outdoors under cotton cloth cages into which were introduced a certain number of viruliferous aphids; the experiment was continued for 7 years. Very susceptible varieties were completely defoliated, as the aphid population increased to huge numbers in such cases. At the end of the experiment, 115 varieties and 10 wild species had been tested and classified. It is interesting to note that, among leading varieties, Katahdin and Netted Gem were very susceptible, Triumph, Chippewa, Erie, Cobbler, Mohawk, Pontiac, Red McClure, Rural, Russet Rural, Sebago, Sequoia, White Rose, and *S. demissum* susceptible, Green Mountain, Red Warba, and Warba tolerant, British Queen, Houma, Up-to-Date, and several wild species resistant, and *S. polyadenium* immune. The author notes some similarity between susceptibility to aphid injury and susceptibility to leaf hopper injury in these varieties.

Internal mahogany browning is a serious defect which develops in low-temperature storage in Maine and other cool-temperature areas. Some varieties and seedlings, particularly those susceptible to leaf roll, are especially subject to it. Folsom (1947) found that predisposition to internal browning is inherited and that Chippewa and Katahdin are even more predisposed to it than Green Mountain. He recommends that breeding stocks and new seedlings be tested for susceptibility to this weakness before they are introduced to the commercial trade.

Technique of Hybridization

Artificial or controlled cross pollination of potato flowers is neither difficult nor mysterious, once the essentials are learned. It is done best in the early morning or evening when the air is still and preferably cool. A technique for use in hybridizing potato flowers was described by Stuart (1921) about the time the national breeding program was being developed. The following procedure is the one generally used:

(1) Select plants to be used as parents. (2) Remove anthers from blossoms (emasculation) of plant to be used as female parent about 24 to 48 hours before blossoms would open; use tweezers for this operation after forcing back petals to expose anthers. (3) Enclose emasculated flowers in small, 1 pound, cellophane bags, including some foliage to protect the style and stigma which will emerge later. (4) Apply pollen to stigma 24 to 48 hours after emasculation. Blossoms to supply pollen are collected from male parent plants about when the pores at the end of the anther sacs open. These are placed in envelopes, each envelope containing flowers from one variety or type of male parent. Pollen is removed by pushing back the corolla and holding it with the thumb and forefinger of the left hand, removing the pistil with tweezers and jarring the pollen from the anthers laid over the thumbnail. The sack is removed from the female parent flower while pollen is being applied. (5) Attach appropriate label to pollinated flower and leave flower under bag for a week or ten days. (6) Remove bag and note whether cross has been successful as indicated by swelling of ovary at base of style. (7) If cross is successful, enclose developing fruits in cheesecloth sack, and tie sack to stem of plant to protect against wind damage. Allow seed balls to remain until slightly yellow; the color indicates ripeness and time for harvest.

Seed Balls

Accidentally or naturally produced seed balls are of interest mainly to those desirous of originating new varieties. The potato being of hybrid origin, varieties obtained from the seed ball are variable and may or may not resemble the parent plant. It is very seldom that varieties of greater commercial value than those already in use are obtained in this way. Examination of the fruits may show that they contain few or no viable seeds; for example, the Rural type seldom produces seed which will germinate. Fruits of Katahdin and other new varieties may contain 50 to 300 viable seeds.

The best procedure in handling the seed balls is to let them wilt a few days, then crush them, and place the resulting pulp in warm water, allowing it to stand several days for fermentation. Fermentation separates the seed from the pulp. Stirring occasionally will cause the seed to fall to the bottom while the pulp will float. The pulp and solution may then be removed and the remaining seed washed and spread upon wire screen or cheesecloth, rather than paper, for drying.

The cured seed should be planted in flats or flower pots at least 2 months before potato planting time. The seed being very similar to tomato seed should be handled in the same manner. Plant very shallow in the flat using fine-screened soil on the surface. After planting, water should be applied with a sprinkling can. Usually 2 years are required before the seedling tubers reach sufficient size to tell whether they have any commercial value. Thousands of seedlings have been grown, but only a few found worthy of commercial planting.

Testing Seedlings

The results of breeding must be measured by growing, testing, and evaluating the seedlings. Experiment station workers have found this work to be time-consuming, laborious, exacting, and expensive. Efficiency calls for careful and thorough observation and recording of those characters which together make a variety worthy or unworthy. Many good names have been wasted on seedlings which soon passed out of production.

Stuart (1915) outlined a procedure for testing seedlings where thousands are handled annually. For plants to be set in the field in early May, the seed should be sown in the greenhouse or hotbed in flats in late March. The transplants are usually set in rows 3 feet apart and 2½ feet apart in the row the first year. This gives each plant a chance to develop its full normal habit. Uprightness of stems, a fairly compact foliage to control weed growth, and good vigor are desirable characters. The second year and thereafter, the seedling tubers are spaced at least no farther apart than 18 inches in the row. Number, shape, and yield of tubers, smoothness of skin, and length and extent of stolon growth are important characters to be evaluated annually for consistency of performance.

Clonal Selection

By definition, a clone is the progeny of a vegetatively propagated individual. Such progeny should breed true or reproduce the parental characters except as aberrant forms occur by mutation. To interpret and apply the definition strictly, potato improvement by selection within a clone or clonal line is impossible. Earlier than 1920, much emphasis was placed on this type of selection as a means of improving seed stocks. Growers were encouraged to practice some form of selection and to maintain seed plots in which to isolate and test their selections for yield and freedom from disease. In many cases, this selection appeared to result in some improvement. Assuming that the increase in yield was significant, it was probably the result either of the isolation of higher-yielding strains or biotypes appearing originally as mutations or of partial elimination of tubers carrying virus disease. At the present time, most of our commercial seed stocks represent the progeny of a tuber-unit or tuber line which probably was propagated in a program of seed certification. Stuart (1915) said: "In the improvement of the potato by selective methods alone, the selectionist is limited to the natural or accidental or discontinuous variations within the variety itself . . . but few real valuable variations ordinarily occur within a commercial variety."

Folsom, Owen and Smith (1931) systematically tested healthy seed stocks of Green Mountain variety from several states and Canada, and from high- and low-yielding tuber-unit progenies of the same strain of Green Mountain. Although significant differences in yield and tuber type were obtained in some instances, their relative rank was not maintained in subsequent years. Strain differences were generally smaller than differences due to location in the field, method of planting, seasonal weather, and cultural practices. They concluded that "one healthy commercial strain is not to

be preferred to another and tuber-unit selection is not to be recommended, at least in commercial practice."

Some commercial seed growers still practice tuber-unit selection,
and many who do not use the results to measure yield differences
find this an effective way to reduce virus disease and weak plants in
their foundation seed stock. Livermore (1933) was a strong pro-
ponent of the tuber-unit selection method of isolating and maintaining superior yielding strains of seed. He attempted to refute
the implication of many authors that differences in yield between
selections from seed stock of a given variety can be attributed to
differences in content of virus disease. Furthermore, he pointed out
that "in the score or more of tuber-unit selection plots planted each
year on the farms of growers of certified seed potatoes in New York,
it is not at all unusual to find diseased strains that outyield healthy
ones." Whatever the limitations to improvement by clonal selection
may be, a well-managed seed plot in which progenies of single tuber
selections are planted in tuber-units for isolation of diseased or
mutating specimens seems appropriate for the seed grower.

Methods of Selection and Testing

Various procedures have been followed in attempts to improve
potatoes by selection, some almost wholly ineffective, others giving
reliable results.

Mass selection was a term applied to the practice of choosing for
seed from the field or storage bin the best-looking tubers and storing
them together as one lot. This assumed that the shape and type
characters of the selected tubers would maintain in the ensuing
crop. However, shape differences are usually due to differences in
soil and climatic conditions during the growth period and therefore represent fluctuating variations which are not heritable.

Mass-hill selection is a system in which choice is based on yield,
freedom from disease, and other plant characters exhibited by the
entire plant at harvest time. Hills so selected are put together for
planting the following year.

Pedigree-hill selection differs from mass-hill selection only in
the fact that the progeny of each hill is tested separately. This should
be more efficient in that only those hill or plant progenies which
reproduce their desirable characters are saved for seed. It provides
a method of eliminating inferior units.

Later, the tuber-unit method of testing and selection was developed. This assumes possible heritable differences between tubers of the same plant, and, instead of testing the entire hill progeny, a single tuber is planted in four cut pieces in adjacent hills. By leaving an extra space in the row between units, it is easy to observe plant differences and disease, all of which facilitates roguing the undesirable units. The tuber-unit method of testing is the most effective yet devised, and it has resulted in many stocks of certified seed which are today the progeny of a single tuber properly called a tuber line. To avoid the necessity of using an entire year for testing as in

Fig. 129. A randomized test plot of potato seedlings ready for harvest in northern New York. (Plant Breeding Dept., Cornell Univ.)

the case of the tuber-unit seed plot, a method of tuber indexing was developed by F. M. Blodgett at Cornell University. By this method, a single eyepiece is cut from each tuber and planted in the greenhouse to observe virus disease or other abnormality during the winter season. Only those tubers which in the winter test are proved to be healthy are planted in the tuber-unit plot the following year. This method of testing has been very efficient in developing foundation seed stocks, especially where the parent material is limited and expensive.

Yield Tests

The rapid introduction of new varieties and strains has necessitated comparative yield tests annually, under widely differing conditions. Studies to determine the technique most likely to give reliable results have been made at a number of experiment stations. There is general agreement that single-row plots are satisfactory. There is less agreement as to best length of row and number of replications. Small plots, relatively short rows, randomized arrangement, and a sufficient number of replications are required for reasonable accuracy, according to most investigators. Four replications of single-row plots, each 25 hills long and randomized, seem to be the minimum requirement, although up to 10 replications will increase the odds for significance. Numerous tests to measure the influence on yield of missing hills have been made. At least 40 per cent of the yield loss caused by a single skip may be made up by the two plants adjacent to the skip. To attempt to correct yields for losses due to missing hills involves the introduction of serious errors. No attempt to correct yield should be made. When the percentage of missing hills is very great, the yield results should be ignored.

Certified Seed Testing

The production of certified seed potatoes was briefly discussed in Chapter 6. Although seed may qualify for certification so far as the field and bin inspections are concerned, ultimate certification is sometimes contingent on results of a test of samples planted in Florida or some other southern state. Disease readings on plants in early stages of growth during the late winter season make it possible to determine how much virus disease was contracted during the previous season and whether the seed should be used even though certified. This southern testing of northern-grown seed has been a benefit to the entire potato industry.

REFERENCES

Adams, Jean Burnham. Aphid resistance in potatoes. Amer. Potato Jour. 23, No. 1, 1946.
Becker, Catherine L. Inheritance studies in the interspecific cross *Solanum demissum* Lindl. × *S. tuberosum* L. Jour. Agr. Research 59, No. 1, 1939.

Folsom, Donald, F. R. Owen, and Hugh B. Smith. Comparisons of apparently healthy strains and tuber lines of potatoes. Maine Agr. Exp. Sta. Bul. 358, 1931.

Folsom, Donald. Inheritance of predisposition of potato varieties to internal mahogany browning of the tubers. Amer. Potato Jour. 24, No. 9, 1947.

Hayes, H. K., and F. R. Immer. Methods of Plant Breeding: Potato Improvement, New York: McGraw-Hill Book Company, Inc., 1942.

Johnstone, Francis E., Jr. Chromosome doubling in potatoes induced by colchicine treatment. Amer. Potato Jour. 16, No. 11, 1939.

Krantz, F. A., and Harold Matson. Periderm and cortex color inheritance in the potato. Jour. Agr. Research 52, No. 1, 1936.

Krantz, F. A., Catherine L. Becker, and Z. M. Fineman. Incidence and inheritance of pollen sterility in the potato. Jour. Agr. Research 58, No. 8, 1939.

Krantz, F. A., and Carl J. Eide. Resistance to common scab of potatoes in parental clones and in their hybrid progenies. Amer. Potato Jour. 25, No. 8, 1948.

Livermore, J. R. Bud selection. Amer. Potato Jour. 10, No. 2, 1933.

Longley, A. E., and Clark, C. F. Chromosome behavior and pollen production in the potato. Jour. Agr. Research 41, No. 12, 1930.

Reddick, Donald. Development of blight immune varieties. Amer. Potato Jour. 20, No. 5, 1943.

Salaman, R. N. Male sterility in potatoes a dominant Mendelian character. Jour. Linn. Soc. (London) Bot. 39, 301–302, 1910.

Stevenson, F. J., E. S. Schultz, C. F. Clark, Lillian Cash, and Reiner Bonde. Breeding for resistance to late blight in the potato. Phytopath. 27, No. 11, 1937.

Stuart, William. Potato breeding and selection. U.S. Dept. Agr. Bul. 195, 1915.

Stuart, William. Potato breeding, selection and seed development work in the United States. Inter. Potato Conf. Report, Royal Hort. Soc. (London), Nov., 1921.

Tolaas, A. G. Developments in potato breeding. Amer. Potato Jour. 24, No. 7, 1947.

Werner, H. O. Relation of photoperiod and intensity of supplemental light to the production of flowers and berries in the greenhouse by several varieties of potatoes. Jour. Agr. Research, 64, No. 5, 1942.

CHAPTER 17

Economics of Production

POTATO PRODUCTION as a business enterprise can be considered a success only to the extent that it is profitable. Practices which affect an increase in acre yield are profitable up to a point of diminishing returns. Beyond this, the additional cost of production necessary to increase yield merely reduces the net income from the potato enterprise.

Like other crops which have a relatively high cost of production, the potato enterprise involves considerable risk. The main factors of risk are unfavorable weather, disease and insect pests, high costs and uncertain supply of seasonal harvest labor, overinvestment in storage and equipment, and rapidly declining farm prices. The financially successful grower must have the foresight and the business acumen necessary to cope with the risks as well as a knowledge of how to produce high yields of good-quality potatoes.

Buying a Potato Farm

To use the term potato farm implies that its operator plans to derive most of his income from selling potatoes grown on it. Currently, an increasing proportion of the total crop is being produced in larger acreage units on fewer farms. This trend is consistent with the more efficient growing of potatoes by confining them to large, level fields of well-adapted soil. Many experienced growers have migrated from well-established potato areas to other areas which would provide these favorable conditions nearer to good markets and with relatively low land taxes. Such growers have a pioneering attitude and do not feel tied to the farm where they were reared. There is always danger that overenthusiasm may lead to purchase of heavy, poorly drained soil, a condition that may be the reason why the land is for sale. The mistake of buying such land for potato production can only lead to disappointment and perhaps bankruptcy.

Fall or early spring are good seasons to prospect for a potato farm. It is then that one can best judge depth of soil and natural drainage conditions by noting where melting snow or water in low places does not drain away. The use of a soil augur to inspect color and texture of subsoil, and the advice of local extension agencies are good safeguards, and they cost little or nothing.

The location of a potato farm should be such that an average of about 4 inches of rainfall per month, or 1 inch per week, will be available through the growing season. Information on rainfall from the nearest weather station is usually but not always reliable. Local areas sometimes suffer from drought even though they are in a region of ample precipitation. An ample supply of water for irrigation can sometimes supplement the rainfall deficiency.

Suitable soil, along with ample rainfall, is of primary importance in buying a potato farm. Such soil must be friable, loamy, or well-aerated to a depth of at least 8 inches and underlain with well-drained or open subsoil. A soil reaction of approximately pH 5.0 is preferred. A high-lime soil or one of pH 5.6 to 7.0 will give no better yield or market quality, and it may cause difficulty in the control of scab. A soil too acid for potatoes can be easily and cheaply improved by liming, but one that is naturally of relatively high pH value cannot be cheaply acidified. Well-drained, acid soil of good structure and texture may be covered with goldenrod, paintbrush, berry briars, and other acid-tolerant plants when not under cultivation, but such land may be well suited to potato production. Natural fertility is not of primary importance in choosing a potato farm. The available mineral nutrients lacking in the soil can be provided in the form of commercial fertilizer more cheaply than by paying much higher prices for land of a high fertility level.

Other important considerations in buying potato land are elevation, large, level fields, nearness to consuming centers, and good highways or good trucking or railroad facilities. Growers in Maine and in Idaho are so far from market that transportation costs represent a larger fraction of the consumer's dollar, and consequently a smaller return to the grower, than is the case with New Jersey, Long Island, and Pennsylvania growers. As of October 1, 1935, the Aroostook County Council (Maine) published figures showing that, of the Boston jobber's price, less than one-half represented cash paid to the grower.

Cash Receipts in Relation to Location

The farm value per bushel of potatoes varies between states and regions according to distance to market and according to seasonal competition between new and old crop supplies. This relationship is fairly well illustrated by the 1947 total crop cash receipts and receipts per bushel in fifteen important potato states as shown in table 60.

TABLE 60. CASH RECEIPTS AND AVERAGE FARM PRICE PER BUSHEL FOR POTATOES BY LEADING STATES, 1947.

State	Total Cash Receipts (in Thousand Dollars)	Total Production (in Thousand Bushels)	Cash Receipts (per Bushel)
Maine	$ 82,693	62,790	$1.32
California	58,800	37,260	1.58
New York	43,635	33,090	1.32
Idaho	36,867	28,600	1.29
Pennsylvania	23,292	17,985	1.30
Colorado	20,888	19,240	1.08
North Dakota	18,647	20,100	0.92
Michigan	15,925	12,390	1.28
Florida	14,561	3,272	4.45
Oregon	14,001	10,140	1.38
Virginia	12,598	9,450	1.33
Minnesota	11,664	14,520	0.80
Washington	11,449	8,840	1.29
North Carolina	9,544	9,216	1.04
Texas	8,142	4,536	1.80
United States	$551,499	384,407	$1.43

The average farm price per bushel is relatively high in Florida, Texas, and California, because the crop is marketed early and at a season when supplies in the surplus states are low and the public preference is for new potatoes. Colorado, Minnesota, and North Dakota suffer the disadvantage of being a long distance from market and of competition with a late surplus crop in other more favorably situated states. North Carolina and Virginia with early new-crop potatoes usually average a relatively high farm price, but in 1947 they suffered from a glutted market and unfavorable market conditions at harvest time. The farm price for Maine potatoes averaged as high as that for New York and Pennsylvania probably because it was a surplus-crop year, and because the Maine product was better graded.

Capital Investment

Such items as land, buildings, machinery, equipment, livestock, feed, and other supplies used in producing the crop make up what is commonly called capital investment. Actual total investment is not so important as balance between productive and unproductive capital. In such intensive areas as Long Island, New York, Aroostook County, Maine, Kern County, California, and Monmouth County, New Jersey, where acreages are large and land values rather high, there is little danger of overcapitalization in buildings and equipment. This danger is much greater in such producing areas as upstate New York, Pennsylvania, Michigan, and Wisconsin.

When potato prices are high, some growers become overenthusiastic and assume heavy debt obligations which may have to be paid in a later period of low prices and deflated dollars. This is especially true when expensive storages are built and machinery bought. Schrumpf (1935) made a rather thorough economic study of the potato industry of Aroostook County, Maine, for the years 1928–1930. The average capital investment for 165 farms is shown in table 61.

TABLE 61. CAPITAL INVESTMENT ON 165 AROOSTOOK COUNTY FARMS (AVERAGE), 1928–1930.

Item	Investment in Dollars	Investment in Per Cent
Real estate	$24,168	83.9
Machinery	2,262	7.8
Livestock	1,374	4.8
Feed and supplies	1,011	3.5
Total	$28,815	100.0

On the 165 farms, 50 per cent of the real estate was in crop land, 17.4 per cent in dwellings, 12.8 per cent in barns and 5.9 per cent in potato storage houses.

Economic Acreage Unit

The smallest acreage of potatoes which can be operated economically, efficiently, and at a profit varies with several factors. The minimum efficient unit is larger than formerly because, however small, it is in competition with larger units operated more efficiently. Size of business in relation to efficiency of operation must be measured at least partly in terms of efficiency of use of man labor and equipment. This is true because man labor is the largest single item in the cost of production. Even though man labor is expensive, one cannot afford to invest in expensive labor-saving machinery unless he grows enough acres to justify the investment. It is doubtful if a grower can afford to purchase a new planter, sprayer, duster, or digger if he operates less than 5 acres of potatoes. An efficient sprayer is especially expensive, and its cost cannot be justified if it is to be used on less than 10 acres. Cost account studies show that, generally, as size of potato acreage per farm increases, cost of production, returns, and profits per acre also increase. Even though the potato crop in recent years has shown a relatively good return for each acre produced, a good living is possible only with a large acreage, if potatoes are the principal cash crop.

Cost of Production

A complete and accurate record of all costs chargeable to the potato enterprise is necessary for an efficiency study, so that returns for each hour of labor can be reckoned and it can be determined whether potato growing compares favorably with other farm enterprises. Comparing cost records also furnishes a means of showing the good and bad economic periods and the factors which most influence net returns to the grower. For complete cost account records, such items as interest on capital investment, taxes, insurance, and depreciation on buildings, and depreciation on machinery and equipment should be included. Labor is charged at the rate necessary when it is hired. Stable manure is charged usually at 40 per cent of its cost if applied directly to the crop, 30 per cent if one year removed, 20 per cent if two years and 10 per cent if three years before the crop is planted. Cash costs of machinery repair are charged as made, and the cost of machinery is allocated according to its average life duration.

Actual cost records are of little value except as used to measure labor income, returns per hour of labor or wages of the operator, and profit per acre and per bushel. A low acre cost of production does not indicate either profit or efficiency. Usually costs increase as yields and profits increase. For the 5-year period 1930–1934 in Michigan, Aylesworth (1935) compared the cost of producing table stock on 214 farms with that of producing certified seed on 167 farms. The cost of growing and harvesting an acre of table potatoes averaged $39.61, that of certified seed $79.38, or about double. Since the average yield of certified seed was nearly double that of the table stock, the cost per bushel was 50 cents, or only 8 cents higher. The total higher cost of producing certified seed was due to a labor cost over 50 per cent higher, a seed cost nearly three times higher, and a fertilizer cost over four times higher. These figures indicate that growers of table potatoes may well follow most of the methods practiced by seed growers. Williamson (1940) published the results of 30 years of potato cost accounts on New York farms; these are summarized by 5-year periods in table 62.

TABLE 62. COSTS AND RETURNS FROM POTATO GROWING ON 848 NEW YORK COST ACCOUNT FARMS.*

Five-Year Period	Total No. of Accounts	Avg. Acreage per Farm	Avg. Yield per Acre (Bushels)	Avg. Total Cost per Acre	Avg. Profit per Bushel	Avg. Labor per Acre (Hours)	Return per Hour of Labor
1914–1918	130	5.4	111	$ 86	$0.17	91	$0.49
1919–1923	122	3.8	141	122	0.11	99	0.51
1924–1928	142	9.8	150	124	0.31	85	0.89
1929–1933	190	22.9	177	100	0.10	76	0.52
1934–1938	147	20.8	191	87	0.09	79	0.50
1939–1943	117	25.5	232	123	0.26	87	1.08
30 years	848	14.7	167	$107	$0.17	86	$0.67

* Data for 1939–1943 supplied by C. D. Kearl, Dept. of Agricultural Economics, Cornell University.

The data in table 62 are mostly for farms in upstate New York where yields are much lower than on Long Island. They indicate that average yields have consistently increased, and that costs and returns have fluctuated rather widely. Nearly 90 hours of labor are required to grow and harvest an acre of potatoes. The average return per hour of labor was $0.67, ranging from 49 cents to $1.08 by 5-year periods.

Potatoes have returned an average hourly wage rate that exceeds that of most other farm enterprises. Labor is the largest single cost item. Tablante (1948) in a study of New York cost accounts for the period 1942–1945 reported that an average of 93 hours were needed to grow and harvest an acre of potatoes. Of this total 45 hours, or about one-half, were used in digging and picking up the crop which averaged 226 bushels to the acre.

One of the most recent economic studies of potato production was made by Campbell (1948) on 205 farms in the northern Steuben area of New York. The acreage involved was 3184 and represented about 33 per cent of the total potato acreage of this important area. This study showed that size of acreage unit per farm was the most important single factor influencing costs, returns, and profit per acre. Grouping the farms by acreage of potatoes from 3–7 acres to 50 or more acres, returns per acre ranged from $195 to $327, cost per acre from $159 to $215, and profit per acre from $36 to $112. The yield of potatoes averaged somewhat higher from the larger acreage units and apparently resulted from higher expenditure for seed and fertilizer.

It is rare indeed that a carefully kept record of costs and returns in potato growing on a large scale and on a single farm is available. Through the courtesy of H. R. Talmage (1948) of Riverhead, Suffolk County, Long Island, the summary of such a record is presented in table 63.

Until 1882, potato growing on Long Island was not a commercial enterprise. Farm acreages of this crop seldom exceeded that necessary to supply the family. About that time, the shovel plow or middlebuster was introduced as a means of digging potatoes. This made it economically possible to grow several acres and to market the crop in New York and Connecticut cities across Long Island Sound. The average acreage per farm in both Suffolk and Nassau

TABLE 63. COSTS AND RETURNS FROM POTATO GROWING FOR 50
YEARS, BY DECADES, ON A SUFFOLK COUNTY, L.I., FARM.

Ten-Year Period	Avg. Yield per Acre (Bushels)	Avg. Farm Price per Bushel	Receipts per Acre	Avg. Cost per Acre	Avg. Profit per Acre
1898–1907	201	$0.52	$107	$ 51	$ 56
1908–1917	185	0.75	145	79	66
1918–1927	232	1.13	260	175	85
1928–1937	217	0.67	136	132	4
1938–1947	355	0.95	336	195	141

Counties now averages well above 50, and nearly all of the adapted soil is devoted to potatoes. Proximity to good markets, a long growing season favorable to high yields, a soil conducive to high culinary and high market quality, and the introduction of labor saving equipment are factors which together have made Long Island one of the largest and most intensive producing areas in the United States. Continuous cropping to potatoes apparently has not depleted the soil—rather, by constant attention to quality of seed, good spray practice, and a steady increase in the rate of applying fertilizer, the average acre yields have increased. Cost of production has increased, but yields have kept pace so that, except for depression years, returns have been profitable. Using the Talmage farm as an example for this locality, the data in table 63 show that in the depression years of the early 1930's farm prices were low, cost of production was slightly reduced, and yields were cut, with the result that the margin of profit was almost nullified. In contrast to this, there have been decades when the potato enterprise showed a good profit. Such years occurred during and immediately following the periods of both World Wars.

Potatoes in the Home Garden

Whether to include potatoes in the home garden should depend on a number of factors. If space is very limited, other vegetables the quality of which depends more on garden freshness and which are more perishable should have priority. Potatoes are readily available in food stores at all seasons, and usually, they are better than can be grown in the garden. When the garden soil is heavy, when its reaction is favorable to scab, or when it contains much manure or decomposing organic matter, it is difficult to grow tubers which are free from injury by scab, millipedes, slugs and scab gnats. Better potatoes can be grown more efficiently under commercial conditions. Garden production is appropriate when conditions are favorable, space is ample, and good potatoes are not available when wanted. In deficit areas, new potatoes are sometimes scarce and expensive, and an early variety grown in the garden is sometimes appropriate under those conditions. When it is, the gardener should make certain to plant good seed of a suitable variety and be prepared to control disease and insect pests. Early-maturing varieties possessing scab and blight resistance are difficult to find. Disease-resistant varieties are usually late in maturity.

Co-operative Use of Equipment

To grow potatoes efficiently requires the use of expensive equipment. In localities where the average acreage per farm is 5 or less, it may be advisable to arrange for the co-operative ownership of a planter, sprayer, duster, and digger. This distributes and reduces the expense and ensures getting the work done. Difficulties to foresee, however, are responsibility for care and repair of the equipment and the fact that all may want to use the machine at the same time. Perhaps the best plan is for one person to own the machine and rent it to others according to a definite rental agreement. Co-operative spray rings in New York and Pennsylvania are an example of how to get potato spraying done efficiently by a large group of small growers. In this case, one individual owns and operates the sprayer and serves the members of the group according to a contract agreement. The same plan may well be extended to include the use of other expensive equipment.

REFERENCES

Aroostook County Council. Long-time agricultural program for Aroostook County (Maine), 1936.
Aylesworth, P. F. An economic study of the potato enterprise in Michigan. Mich. Agr. Exp. Sta. Special Bul. 267, 1935.

Campbell, Joe R. Costs and returns in producing potatoes, Northern Steuben area, New York, 1946. Cornell Univ., Dept. Agr. Econ. A.E. 657, 1948.

Schrumpf, William E. A study of the organization and management of potato farms in Aroostook County, Maine. Maine Agr. Exp. Sta. Bul. 378, 1935.

Tablante, N. B. Labor requirements for potatoes. Cornell Univ. Farm Economics No. 163, Sept., 1948.

Talmage, H. R. Potato costs and returns for 50 years on one Long Island farm. Personal correspondence, Sept., 1948.

Williamson, Paul. Twenty-five years of farm cost accounts. Cornell Extension Bul. 439, 1940.

Index